DIS TUR BING THE BODY

DISTURBING THE BODY

EDITED BY NICI WEST

Copyright info
Published by Boudicca Press March 2021
Edited by Nici West
Proofread by Katie Anderson-Morrison
Typeset by Vince Haig

ISBN: 978-1-9160290-2-6

Welcome to Disturbing the Body, a collection of body-themed speculative autobiographies from women writers exploring moments when the body goes wrong, misbehaves, is disrupted or disturbed.

Disturbing the Body takes you through a menagerie of female-led experiences and fraught relationships with the body. From Verity Holloway's spiraling hallucinations after a major heart operation to Louise Kenward's disorienting experience with chronic illness and Irenosen Okojie's terrifying battle with the Covid-19 virus. Read these pieces with respect and an open heart, for it's not often that we get to hear such unfiltered and speculative exploration of true experiences, especially from women.

This is a sister anthology to *Disturbing the Beast*, 2019, a collection of weird fiction stories by some of the best women writers in the UK that also explores lesser talked about female-centered topics.

Take care of yourselves, and read on.

From Boudicca Press

CONTENTS

A note from Verity Holloway [9]
A note from Louise Kenward [11]

Oh, Oramorph! And the
First Drafts of God
VERITY HOLLOWAY
[13]

Underland
LOUISE KENWARD
[91]

Mary Celeste
NATASHA KINDRED
[29]

Yolk
CHIKODILI EMELUMADU
[101]

Her Entire Body of Work
LAUREN BROWN
[35]

And the Forever House
LAURA ELLIOTT
[109]

Christalien
NINA K. FELLOWS
[55]

The Sisterhood of
Broken Dolls
BEVERLEY BUTCHER
[119]

Phantasmagoria
ABI HYNES
[69]

The Animal at My Chest
JANE HARTSHORN
[131]

Subnival, or: Sister, Teach
Me About Time!
MARION MICHELL
[87]

Aslym
IRENOSEN OKOJIE
[139]

Biographies [149]
Supporters [153]
About Boudicca Press [155]
About Disturbing the Beast [157]
Acknowledgements [159]

A NOTE FROM VERITY HOLLOWAY

This anthology was a collaborative effort from the start. In the weeks following my open-heart surgery, I was coming to terms with a radically altered body that no longer felt like my own. As a writer, I deal in fantasy and horror – what's more fantastical and horrifying than major surgery? – and so I found myself making sense of the ordeal through a mix of autobiography and the speculative fiction techniques I felt at home with. Chatting to Louise Kenward and other writers, it became apparent that many of us had done the same, then abandoned the pieces, unsure of what to do with them. In processing our experiences of illness, disability and trauma, we had all produced writing too weird for the confessional essay crowd, and too personal to disguise as fiction. We sensed a collection brewing, and, thanks to Boudicca Press, we found a home for it.

Inhabiting a body is an inherently strange thing. Our physical shells are magnets for outside expectations, and inevitably those societal and political forces acting on the body encroach upon our inner worlds. It's a conflict we all have to come to terms with. Our bodies will all be disrupted, by accident, design, misfortune or the passage of time, and yet, so often, external demands are placed on our stories – demands for inspiration, for a happy ending or a touch of wisdom. In telling the story of our own troublesome bodies, we are tacitly expected to offer something as payment.

Our hope for Disturbing The Body was that women writers would feel free to express their perceptions of their bodies as creatively as they pleased, resisting the urge to package those experiences in neatly stacked boxes or feel the need to apologise for their unique, beautiful, touching – and sometimes hilarious – strangeness.

Verity Holloway, 2021

A NOTE FROM LOUISE KENWARD

The role of chance and coincidence is a pertinent parallel for the development of a book that grew out of a Twitter conversation one Sunday afternoon. The role of chance in becoming unwell, experiencing trauma and living with disability is a reality of being human: we all hold two passports, a dual citizenship of the 'kingdom of the well and...the kingdom of the sick' (Susan Sontag, 1977, *Illness as metaphor*, Penguin) and it is this vulnerability we all carry and so often deny. Increasingly these worlds are indistinct – as chronic illness levels rise, as the impact of serious illness lasts beyond its presence in our bodies, as we survive life-threatening conditions – but at what cost? In a landscape now scarred with Covid-19, we are confronted with how unexpectedly but consistently illness knocks at our door.

Now more than ever we need words and language as we try to grapple with these complex things.

For so long the narrative of illness has been of medicine, the medical model and of doctors' voices. Considerable harm is done through a lack of understanding and through seeing illness through only one lens. It is a narrative of polarities: of health and sickness, kill or cure, life and death. There is much more in between and within.

This is a collection of exciting new writing told by the person from the other side of the desk, and it is a far more nuanced tale than you might find in your medical records. This is the richness of experience and the depth of knowledge you can only learn from those who have trekked in these places. I am delighted to be a part of this project to bring these stories to you, subverting the narrative and throwing up the unexpected, adding something new in telling things 'on the slant' to this growing genre.

Louise Kenward, 2021

OH, ORAMORPH!
AND THE FIRST
DRAFTS OF GOD

VERITY HOLLOWAY

SUBNIVAL, OR: SISTER, TEACH ME ABOUT TIME!
by Marion Michell, page 87, correction issued March 2021

Marion Michell's 'SUBNIVAL, OR: SISTER, TEACH ME ABOUT TIME!' (page 87) assembles an artist who is obsessed with the production of a stare, a woman whose life is severely impacted by disease, and a fairy tale figure who will not speak until an evil spell is reversed. Apologies: due to a typesetting error, the formatting of the artist's part which differentiated a narrative voice was lost.

The following paragraphs should have been printed in bold:

Page 87
somewhere in-between. things hovering on a margin, a brink, about to fall. the artist tries to squeeze time into a photograph. not just a moment, but a passage. she photographs herself swaying: limbs dissolve in a flutter, her mouth disintegrates, she splits in two and two again, into ever fainter copies of herself.

she tries to arrest movement in film. halt the passage of time, extend moments at her will. while the camera skims his face. K sits motionless, his breath flat. when she checks the footage later, she finds a full minute of well-nigh stillness. she will edit out the blinks, produce a loop with a continuous, seamless stare.

Page 88
she sits in the editing suite for hours, trying not to blink lest she miss the flap of lashes. one by one she clips them from the video. slowed down, and up close, they look like the synchronised wingbeat of a pair of pinned beasties.

Page 90
imagine a monitor suspended from the ceiling. you look down at the screen as if into a pond. at first glance the upturned face seems lifeless, as in a photograph. don't turn away! by and by the slightest movement of the head, a subtle swallowing motion, a twitch in one eye, become events.

'I like your slippers,' says the nurse, 'I need a pair of those.'

In a few minutes, I will, for all intents and purposes, be dead. I wiggle my feet.

'Thanks. I like sequins.'

I'm in a queue of wheelchairs outside the operating theatre. To my right: a row of men shrivelling into their eighties, their tattoos green stains against white gowns. They've parked us in front of a window, but there's nothing to see. That would be cruel, I guess. A tease. I stare at industrial pipes, red brick, a sliver of sky. Papworth was an isolation hospital once, a place for Edwardians with bloody handkerchiefs. When you look the hospital up, you find grainy photos of gaunt men with crescent moon moustaches playing croquet, the ancestors of my silent, inked companions. It's hard to get to, Papworth, out in the sticks, buried in woodland. A hiding place. Last night on the ward, I watched a heron sail over the trees, a slow and stately phantom.

I am thirty-two years old and I've signed all the paperwork. My heart will be stopped with a solution of potassium, my brain will be cooled, and a man I've met twice will split my rib cage and slip his hand inside. I said goodbye to my friends yesterday. *Good luck with your hardware upgrade*, goes the joke. Verity 2.0. I've signed a permission slip saying they can keep my old aortic root as a teaching aid. I ought to have broken up amicably, been forgiving. It just wasn't going to work, you and me. I don't want it turning up on the doorstep in the night, full of recriminations. *You think you can cast me off? Just because I was going to kill you? Learn to take a joke.*

I look at my pale chest, feel the trip and trill of the rhythms inside. The first draft, the flawed prototype.

When the anaesthetists introduce themselves, I'm looking at a girl. She is escorted in by a nurse, her bald head shining unfairly. She's the only patient younger than me, the only other female, and I try to catch her eye but she stares ahead with the grim serenity of an old hand.

'Is there anything you'd like to know?'

I'll be dead in a few minutes, I want to tell them. The same impulse as saying, *it's my birthday!* A temporary ghost. This place is teeming with ghosts. They had to extend the local churchyard several times in the nineteen-twenties to house all the tubercular dead.

'I read an article. It was about people waking up during surgery.'

The anaesthetist blinks. 'Okay. So. That was the worst thing you could have read.' We all grin. 'It is possible. But only if the anaesthetist isn't doing their job. And we do our job very well. Don't we?' She turns to her colleague, who agrees.

'You'll never be left alone. Not through any of this.'

It's funny, funny is good. I'm the kind of prisoner who jokes on the way to the gallows. *I like to be informed*, I say, scrolling forum posts of wives fretting that Geoff hasn't been the same since the bypass, he's mean and forgetful and she wants the old version back, the one before the upgrade.

But then it's time.

I am wheeled into a frigid antechamber. I worry absurdly that I haven't brought a jumper. Everything is going too fast. A nurse asks me what I do. She's trying to distract me. The anaesthetist prepares the cannula for the first dose of sedative, the one that'll stop me scrambling off the table and making for the window. Did the Edwardians ever make a run for it, I wonder? Pick up their failing lungs, sling them over their shoulders, and disappear into the woods?

She's holding my hand now. I'm babbling about Victorian quackery, vivisection, the ethics of placebos. The sedative is washing through me. What do I do? Nothing of much consequence. Manage *this*. But she means for money, and the most money I've ever made was reading tarot cards to fretting stay-at-home mothers. *I've seen my husband's browser history, should I leave him? I've never felt good enough, should I sell my homemade birthday cards on the Internet?* I love those lonely women at this moment, and I love the nurse holding my hand. I tell her she's wonderful, hardworking, an asset to everyone who meets her.

'You can feel it, can't you?' she says, or words like it. The anaesthetist lifts my wrist to insert the deeper cannula. The hard stuff.

A coloured rectangle slides across my wavering field of vision.

You have drawn the Midazolam card. Twin to the trickster Fentanyl, Midazolam denotes the miasma of memory, the healing power of letting go.

'Just feel free to mess me up,' I mumble. And the deep woods laugh.

*

Huh. They decided not to do it.
Thing down my throat.
Arm. Point. Thing down my. No.

*

When I was ten, my best friend presented me with a certificate. I'm being literal, she cut it out of a composition book, the size of a business card, with official-looking stamps sketched in biro. *This is to certify we can't be friends anymore because you can't climb trees.* Where did they learn? That strength of the legs, the surety of the wrists? It was around that time I started telling everyone I was from a distant planet. I have paperwork of my own, I can point to the gene. When the alien thing ran out of steam, I turned to ghosts. Famously unencumbered by their bodies, the unquiet dead. Letters home from the headmistress: *Verity's stories are upsetting the other children...* Really? I found them comforting. Anyway, those other kids had it easy.

I'm down here. In the rooty mulch. In and out, drifting on a hot wind. After eight hours my eyes crack open and there's a nurse at my side, gently radiating summer garden pink.

'My name is Rose.'

It makes a sickly sort of sense.

My voice is a geriatric creak. 'The girl with a bald head – she's out? Tell her I'm proud of her.'

Rose dabs my brow and holds me with her gaze while I cry.

'My mum died of this,' I whisper.

*

You drew the Dopamine card. Dopamine, given intravenously, is the drug of choice for the treatment of low cardiac output after open-heart surgery for congenital heart disease. The Dopamine card, part of the Major Arcana, represents sunrises, new growth, and communication.

Intimacy blossoms in the brain like jasmine, but no sooner have I learnt Rose's name, she's gone. There are vines inside of me, erupting from my pores. The forest has crept indoors. I am slow to realise it; this is my upgrade. There's a bed and my body is rooted to it. Plastic tendrils emerge from my solar plexus, my neck, my nose, my groin, my wrists.

In the sap, pain.

A doctor and a team of students pass by. I haven't slept in three days.

'Pain?'

'Bad.'

'Where?'

'Everywhere.'

My torso is a mess of brambles. 'You must try to breathe,' someone tells me. Offstage, a dozen dead Edwardians laugh.

The doctors converse behind a curtain. ('Do we use ketamine here?' 'That's kind of hardcore.')

The Ketamine card. Wild horses sleep beneath a fading sun. We heal the present by sacrificing a little future, a little piece of it, less than nothing.

'I'd like to try something,' the lead doctor says, leaning over me. 'We have injections. They block the nerves from talking to the brain. What do you think?'

Yes. Anything.

Epidural. Major Arcana. This too shall suck.

A team of people roll my broken skeleton onto its side. My sternum is lashed together with titanium thread and I feel every stitch and knot as my nerves perform a Frankenstein dance.

I've made a terrible mistake. I'm not ready for this upgrade. It's a pristine tube of woven polyethylene, the new plumbing of my chest. The surgeon said my own arteries were like wet tissue paper. Perhaps I'm incompatible with such synthetic perfection.

They hold me there for a hundred years while they work the needles into my spine. I envy the tubercular ghosts in the halls, the ones whose bones rest in the overflowing cemetery. I don't think they'll accept me now, as I am, with my plastic heart and chainmail bones. That's litter, isn't it, in a churchyard? I'll be swept up with the crushed Coke cans and condom wrappers.

The epidural doesn't touch the pain. They can't understand it. They throw every card they have at it, gas and air, codeine, a Hail Mary of paracetamol I bring up straight away because it's insulting, frankly. Night and day have melted into a fluorescent nothing and someone is talking.

'It says here you've only been receiving half doses of morphine. Would you like to try some more?'

Yes. Anything.

'It might make you sick, but we can give you drugs for that too. Okay?'

Yes. Anything.

And so I draw the last card left in the pack. Oramorph comes in a plastic syringe and is the purplest thing I've ever seen. Funfair purple, forbidden candy purple, the purple of hyperactive children and novelty vodka. High Mass vestments of lurid damask, the Crab Nebula, The Artist Formerly Known

As Papaver Somniferum. And it tastes purple. It slides over your tongue and turns your veins to mines of amethyst. 'Open your mouth, I'm going to pop this under your tongue,' the nurse says, and then – *Gott in Himmel* – PURPLE.

Down we go

*

When I clamber out from the capsized vessel of my body, I've been wheeled into a room of my own. Grey walls, grey floor, grey ceiling, window – window? – forest. It's the first time Verity 2.0 has seen the outside. With the windows open to the cool spring night, I can smell the earth somewhere under all the sweat and iodine. Owls screech, an unseen gathering. I feel privy to something secret.

Oramorph is my diet now. The caterers try to tempt me with ice cream and Maltesers, but everything tastes either of soap or meat, and calories are a poor substitute for my purple deliverance. I stare at the clock as if I might ration my pain. Only four more hours until the next dose. Only three and a half. When night rolls around and the nurses expect me to sleep, the hours stretch out ahead of me, a desert to cross.

I am joined in my vigil by the Watchmen. The cave directly behind my headboard hasn't bothered me until now; it's not as if I can roll over and look inside. The Watchmen are two in number and take turns lumbering out of the rocky opening to swing a torch across my bed, my drips, my monitors. I get to know their weird workings. Sometimes there's a screwup in the schedule and Watchmen come plodding out at the same time. They turn their lights on each other and their clockwork grinds and sticks, leaving them staring with mute incomprehension. *In-tru-der*, they try to say, but they lack the power of speech. Their purpose is only to watch, just as mine as to lie here watching the shadows of the trees etch a broken ladder up the walls.

I hear the trundle of the morning drug trolley. I part my dry lips.

*

Now that I've taken to Oramorph, I receive visitors. Mostly, it's the French girl who drifts languidly in and out of the bathroom. I have no idea who she is – she's never bothered to say *salut* – but I become accustomed to her Breton sweater and black cigarette pants worn just above the ankle. She's enviably gamine, no hips and precious few facial expressions, and she smokes, I realise with the telepathy I seem to have now, because Camus does. The nurses never tell her to stop.

I am yet to look at my chest. When my nurse comes to wash me, The Watchmen sweep their torches over the gauze and tape and I make the half-conscious mistake of glancing down as she opens my Velcro binder. There it all is. The new me. My ruined flesh is the resentful yellow of perished rubber. I see blood, flecks of it, crisscrossing like rusty embroidery. My body is swollen to tightness with kilograms of excess water.

'I'm sorry,' I croak, turning my head as far as the wires in my neck will allow.

'If it helps,' the nurse says gently, 'it's very neat and it's quite low. I see a lot of these.'

I smell a French cigarette. '*Répugnante.*'

It's not my only scar. The surgeon took a vein from my thigh. Leering out from my pyjama shorts, this bypass wound is dark and huge, the colour of a crime scene. I sit on the edge of the bed, sweating and grimacing, trying to raise myself to my feet. It could be three AM. I have no idea, and the owls aren't telling. I've been here forever in my sparkly slippers with my nurse beside me, waiting for me to shuffle another inch. The bathroom is four feet, four continents away, and I will walk there or die trying.

'If you say sorry one more time, I'll smack your bottom.' The nurse is smiling, but then she looks at my machines. 'Your heart rate is nudging two-hundred. I'm sorry, but we have to give it up for tonight.'

The French girl shuttles back and forth – bed to bathroom, window to hall – bland with ennui.

'*Facile.*'

*

A man down the hall is screaming. He keeps it up with impressive diligence. The other patients try to drown him out with their televisions, so my purple-tinted world rings loud with the Antiques Roadshow trumpets shot through by a hammer symphony of agonies. It hurts to laugh.

If you don't move your body, pneumonia sees its chance. Twice a day, a pair of nurses flank me like guards and take the count – one, two, three, *UP!* – as if they're raising a barn. Three seconds on my feet and I'm down again, spent and shuddering.

'Is… he… alright?' I say, nudging my chin towards the corridor, the noise.

'You just concentrate on yourself.'

At teatime, the noise attracts the tiny figure of Madame Tussaud. She trundles in, wearing an austere gown for a solemn task. Soon, my walls are hung with death masks fresh from the guillotine. Waxy kings, dukes, barons. They had to die, her look tells me. Revolution is born of sacrifice. The Watchmen come with their searchlights and together we regard the display of slack mouths and double chins as night ticks down to morning. When the nurses come by to measure my progress, they are pleased with how diligently I'm working on my daily goals of standing, sitting, sweating.

'Some of our older patients hate following instructions. Especially the men. They're the ones who hurt themselves trying silly stunts like rolling over in bed.'

Sure, I think, as the morning's Oramorph comes sailing over me, full spinnakers of violet chiffon. What's a revolution without a little blood?

*

Tuberculosis brings on night sweats. The building tells me that, and the woods outside offer cool agreement. I have them too, though my lungs are merely stunned. Fever. They explain to me the names and functions of the drugs they're pumping into me, but the cards slide across my brain and disintegrate.

I can't read them anymore. The cards, my memories, my own swollen face. There's a pile of magazines on my table, but I can't make sense of them either. I watch my vitals peak and trough on the screens and search for meaning. Perhaps I've lost the knack. Sacrificed it, as Madame Tussaud said. I've given away a piece of my heart, after all.

'You're wasting their time,' drawls the French girl from the bathroom I can't walk to. She is balanced on the edge of the sink, revolving slowly on one pointed toe. 'They all work so hard, and you just lie there. And your skin is bad.'

I was promised charming emaciated Edwardian spirits. Instead, I have this *vache*. But she's right, my skin is worse than a teenager's. My hair is growing at a supernatural pace, as are my nails. The endocrine system is waking up. Finally receiving the right amount of blood, I suppose, though the science is a mystery to me. All I know is the window is open and the trees are rustling in the breeze and I would give anything to be out there, walking, climbing, inhaling, but–

There's a man in the room with me.

'Hi-di-hi!'

He's approaching sixty, the luncheon meat pink of him sweltering against a white polo shirt. He whispers his odd greeting, and my skin is set crawling. I wish the Watchmen were here. When I don't respond, he tries again, smiling wider:

'Nice to see you, to see you nice!'

Why is he whispering? I look for the button for the nurse. It's on his side of the bed.

I try to speak. 'Who are you?'

'88 to 91FM, Steve Wright's Sunday Loooove Songs.'

I can count his fillings. Something is wrong. Surely if I were hallucinating, I'd see something I wanted to, not Steve Who Whispers Horribly. My head is hot and my bones are crying again. Where is my Oramorph?

A sharp pain. The needle in my arm has burst its banks. In seconds the whole limb is Popeye swollen and I'm slapping the call button. Steve, if he was ever here, is gone.

*

Haunted or delirious, I don't get a say in it either way. So when a vicar pulls up a chair I take stock of him with weary scepticism.

He's young and his burly arms are covered in intricate tattoos.

'Can I see?' I ask. It's a ploy to break the mirage, but the chair creaks when he shifts and I can smell the outside on him. Against all this clinical cleanliness, the scents of domesticity stand out. Washing powder, a pet's fur, dinner in front of the television. The man is a reliquary.

'This one's the vision of the valley of the dry bones,' he says, turning his bicep towards me. 'The Lord shows Ezekiel a desert of skeletons and asks him, "Son of man, can these dry bones live?" And then Ezekiel watches as the bones all come together, growing muscles and tendons and skin. "I will put breath in you," said the Lord, "and you will come to life".'

I recall the queue of wheelchairs outside the operating theatre. How long ago was that? Two days? A week? A line of dead men lifted up, stitched and upholstered into a second life. But it hurts, I want to tell the vicar. Resurrection. I can't imagine a future free of pain.

He tells me something profound. I instantly forget it.

*

Whispering Steve comes again after my evening Oramorph, as is his habit. Behind me, the lone Watchman passes his torch over Steve's polo shirt. He's sweaty, and his smile is a shifty one. He probably owns a white van and honks at joggers, I think unkindly, but then I correct myself: there is something incomplete about Steve. The Watchmen are just as hollow, with their flapping, wordless mouths. Even the French Girl's cruel remarks are flimsy to me, wet tissue paper, an old certificate made by a friend I haven't seen in twenty years.

Steve squats by the bed, his head level with mine. "Allo 'allo 'allo?'

'You're not real.'

'Watch and learn, Rodders, watch and learn.'

Whispering Steve turns to the window, at the dark woods. I follow his look as the owls offer a long shriek of encouragement. The window is black. No distant city lights to pine for. Here in our shared isolation, my companions have weight and heft. Whispering Steve misses his wife. His abandonment reeks of meat and soap. The French Girl should, by rights, be performing her boredom in a café somewhere shabby and chic. But this is Cambridgeshire. Pig pens and fenland. No wonder she taunts me and my unworkable legs. She can't leave either.

It comes to me intravenously: they're dumped there. The first drafts. The dry bones. No different to every bad poem I've ever scribbled on a bank statement and lost down the back of a radiator. Human souls, not quite done.

In this busy hospital room, there are no Edwardians. I see the same oak trees they did, swaddled on sun terraces, thinking of distant friends, of better times, of the bathroom and how impossibly far away it is. I see the quaint pastoral wallpaper of stately homes never built. A python shifts in my lap, heavily docile. And in a one, two, three, I am *up* with another nameless nurse at my side and my leg wound bleeding into my sequined slippers and each shuddering step is a zombie shuffle. On the floor, a family of translucent Ancient Egyptians talk loudly over a dinner of beer and bread. I see them in the bathroom mirror, these humans lightly sketched and abandoned out here in the isolation zone. They've come in to see me, the second draft, the one who made the cut.

MARY CELESTE

NATASHA KINDRED

No one knew why a girl would turn into a ship. Quickly, too, almost overnight. They ran ultrasound wands up the strained rigging of her ligaments. They cushioned the creaking masts of her with air boots and painkillers. They pushed her out into the warm waters of the hydrotherapy pool to see if she would float again, but Mary just flooded and sank. They asked her to stand and walk and sit, gazing at the rigid shapes of her landlocked legs, sucking their uniform teeth. They stretched her new tendons into lines of white agony, they made her sleep with her feet strapped at right angles, they x-rayed her knees and spine and bowsprit. Mary submitted to every machine, her voice tucked away in a shell, before being beached in a harbour of Mother's soft sheets.

Salt-soaked wood is the taste in her mouth. Drowned momentarily by milky coffees and orange juice, steak and onions, Greek yoghurt. Too soon, the reek of wet keel in the sun returns. The swell and warp of boats in purgatory, the dull flavour of windless days. Half woman, half wooden, Mary spoons oxtail soup into her mouth. Her lips are thinner than they were before, stripped of their colour and pressed to death. She wraps soft things around her rougher edges, splinters pulling at grey cashmere. When she lies down and closes her eyes, her spirit is filled with slick, silky, illuminated green; she can stretch out her arms and drift in it forever, this secret stretch of shallow sea. She breathes again, the planks of her ribs creaking as they expand, as Mary takes on water.

Her maternal grandfathers aren't wholly to blame; sailors at home suspended in blue momentum, in places that are not places, shorescapes open to interpretation. Blood like that runs clean as air when given room to flow. Cramped in veins that are too small, it gets brackish and stinking, rotting in port. The water has a way of taking revenge when scorned, we are too much fluid and salt ourselves for safekeeping. The ocean makes widows in mountain towns and she can steal children from anywhere. Mary was lucky to escape with her little curse, her split hull and elbow barnacles, her skin shedding paint (one day she woke to find she had razor clams for ankles, each halting step like that of a mermaid trapped in transition – she dropped anchor in bed and stayed there for a year).

Hips to hard deck in an awkward pitch. Hair to limp sails that catch no wind. Muscles to shrouds, mouth to a cannon.

A year adrift in disabled isolation, the taste of samphire grows stronger under her tongue. New limbs groaning to alien currents, things armoured and creeping, seeking gaps in her silence, looking for homes in the chill and the dark. Mary the ghost ship drifted on rudderless, whelks pasting over her coral-pink mouth. When the doctor called, she held the shell of the phone to her ear and heard the clicking of crab legs, like sinister Morse code, she felt the fat being picked off her wide white bones and eaten in blubbery chunks. She hit crush depth and imploded in milliseconds.

Mary listed and rolled with the tide, abandoned ship, an immobile home to ghosts. They offered her walking aids, predicting wheelchairs, and she dragged her splitting soles on

Long John Silver sticks to the corner shop and back, a hundred feet of freedom. The nights are so full when alone at sea; the depth charge of silence, the moon pinned in pieces to roiling cold satin, the constant collapse of 80ft towers. The ocean is horror hunger, naked as knives, just one long primitive tongue.

Mary changed course to some internal shore. Even ghost ships, (and drowned women, and wind-bleached figureheads) can find somewhere to go; lonely scraps of raw, ragged land where gulls ice the sky and time curdles in curling fossils below. Left on her side to the sun, she vomited lobsters. She hoarded shark's teeth like Spanish reales. She swore at the sympathetic eyes of bewildered seals and radiated rage like the reek of bladderwrack. She told the whole story to passing turtles patiently scraping out sandcastle nurseries; their calm, prehistoric therapist's eyes had already seen it all. She shook out her sails and raw-bellied monsters fell out, the wind took the smell of their spindled claws and sour flesh away. She jettisoned jetsam at the sea's lace hem and, joints still inflamed with tidal salt, remains at sea to this day. No first mate. No true North. No port in a storm. Creaking and restless with rare shells for fingernails, her heart is carved into cardinal points. Her neck gleams with the sapphires in her grandfather's blood. Her hair was repainted only last week, the crimson of fresh-boiled crab.

HER ENTIRE
BODY OF WORK

LAUREN BROWN

'What you see here, ladies and gentlemen, is the original rupture.'

Already a hand, not quite raised – just to eye level. High enough for me to either acknowledge or ignore, depending on my whim.

I hate questions.

'Sorry, hi, yes, did you say rupture or rapture?'

'I said rupture. Folks, there'll be time for questions at the end.'

Patronising. Perfect.

A long diagonal scar across the abdomen. There's a thick swerve in the middle, but is otherwise straight. Tightly framed.

I point to the middle of the image.

'This is where the incision would have begun. Avoiding the spleen, stomach itself and other internal organs. Which, if you look at the catalogue, was dangerous terrain in the late 1970s.'

There are ten, maybe eleven artworks in this place and I rarely give tours of the whole lot. I save them for big events like this Open House and significant others.

There are quite a lot here today. I guess that's a good thing. Lucky I'm wearing lipstick and fuck-off earrings: a power move that gives me the sense of authority that I may or may not have.

'This scar is the only remnant of a year-long performance piece between 1977 and 1978. Beginning with Vomit After Every

Meal, then Unable to Keep Food Down and, finally her public work, An Abdominal Hernia at 18 Months.

'It was her debut work, setting up the themes for her entire body of work: ripping, scarification, prosthesis and out-of-body recollection.

The artist herself has said:

"Although no direct memory would have been formed at the time, the stress, anxiety, gag reflex, inability to vomit and relentless questions about the scar in all examinations thereafter created the indelible rupture with all things corporeal."'

Another hand raised. Can't they wait?

'Why is it called Untitled 1978?'

OK, fair question.

'It's alluding to the undocumented name of the procedure she was replicating. Its original subtitle was 'A complex something something plasty: the insertion of a prosthetic esophageal sphincter', but the word sphincter causes confusion, so she left it untitled.'

I turn away from the framed work and lead this group of interested weirdos to the outer East Wing, a veritable Pied Piper.

'Ordinarily, the next piece to be discussed would be these others, in proximity…'

I gesture to some of the works nearby: other tattoos and scars in the sombre burgundy Centre Hall.

'…but Open House is just that, so today's tour is chronological. The next one is described on page 33 in your printed catalogues, or number 19 on the audio guide'

I give them time to refer to it, listening to the flick of pages and faint *boop* of buttons pressed, tracks skipped.

I stride. Detached. Head high. In such stark contrast to the images of the bubbly artist they clutch.

'Many of you will probably relate to this next one.'

Before we even get to the doors of the darkened screening room, I click the remote in my pocket and the audio starts, kids squealing in delight as they grope for a place to sit.

Up and over a brown overstuffed chair, two children – one boy, one girl, chase each other. As one is on the back, the other is on the seat, weighing it down. Up and over. The boy slips a little as he runs around the base and misses the timing – she's already on the back. The chair tips. Up and over, slamming the four-year-old girl on the ground. The video explodes into white light, then into white plaster bandage winding around a red and swollen arm. It transitions again into a thick cast and a tiny hand poking out, resting on her lap as she sits on the gutter outside a small home. A beautiful day, blue skies, a slight breeze, a bird. Shit. Plop. Right on the other arm. The free arm.

The final frame holds on these two arms, one broken, one shat on.

An alarm of childish wailing reeeeeeaaarrrrs and the screen goes black.

You can hear them chuckling in the dark before the house lights smooth up.

'I'm sure you can see why it's called The Indignity…'

Not even a questioning hand, just a naked opinion:

'Not just the indignity of the bird shit, but also of the way the arm was broken, right? Being let down by the boy, too?'

'I can see why you would think that, but in interviews about that reading of the title, the artist cautioned against applying knowledge of later work as context for this one…'

I eye them, knowingly.

'…Although I do think it is an interesting theme that comes up.'

I continue, in my practiced guide voice,

'From 1981, this is also her first work that draws on the language of cinema. Flashes and framing. Narrative and even humour. It's also ephemeral – the work only comes on when you trigger the sensor. There are no indicators otherwise, at least no permanent ones, that it exists.'

They have drifted away. 'Language of cinema' turns them off every time.

My leather-soled shoes clack on the hardwood floor and echo off the high ceilings as we head into a darkened room, still in the central section.

'Now, if you're squeamish or sensitive to graphic images, you might want to wait outside.'

It's a standard warning these days. I don't really give a shit if they are triggered by this crap. They know what kind of show this is. But before we go in, I gather them round.

'Do any of you already know this work?'

One hand goes up. A short guy with a cute quiff and an Hermès neckerchief.

It amazes me how many people who come to this place don't know it. Almost all her other work stems from it. OK, maybe the one in the Western Wing doesn't, but still – I'm annoyed at their ignorance.

'This piece is the crux of almost everything else you'll see today. Again, because this is a chronological tour, rather than thematic, the connections won't be as obvious, but they're there. Maybe we also can cover that at the end.

'Right, you all ready?'

The guy who already knows the work stays behind. I like his style, so I don't judge him too much. Yet.

An installation of broken mirrors and screens. Depending on which angle it is approached, depends what part of the perspective you get. And every one produces vertigo.

I see them all clutch at the frames, then remember Do Not Touch The Artwork and have to steady themselves with arms outstretched and a wobble.

There is an ambulance in one section. Flashing words, like Barbara Krueger or Jenny Holzer: 'YOUR BROTHER' 'AMBULANCE', 'BOOT OF THE CAR' and 'DEAD'. Other sections have front page headlines from the newspaper. The viewer must follow instructions to keep the work moving; they must sit on the lap of a figure known as Absent Mother.

It's a sideshow in there. If they sit, they have to pull a sad face to match the image on a wall, which triggers a photographic flash in order to get off the chair and keep moving through the work. I've seen people do it a hundred times and the look of panic at being flashed and stuck at the same time, surrounded by flashing lights and crowds: this is why kids aren't allowed in. They burst into tears immediately. Adults would like to, but are just relieved to get to the next part of the piece.

A screen on the floor and the dead body of a young boy. Made up in a coffin, it merges with the graphic image of him in a pool of blood and piss and bile, pale and barely breathing, then back to the image of him in a white coffin.

The rest of the room is blacked out and it's just the image on the floor, which is actually two stories down.

If you wait and watch them, like I do each time, you can see them realise how far up they are as they grip the stairs. I wait for them at the bottom of the big black box.

'You'll notice the drop in temperature.' I say, with my kindest concern on.

'Please be careful as you make your way through to the exit. It's dark.'

I have to wait until the last one stumbles through. Which means I need to listen to the final moments of the soundtrack with screaming, door slams and 'I want a divorce!!'.

That's the worst bit about art with a soundtrack. You are forced to listen to it over and over and over again. Most of the time, punters don't even hear it all the way through.

Asphyxiation is usually at the end of the show, so when you come out of that dark, cold depressed space, it's the end and there's a nice welcoming cafe and bookshop and you can buy a t-shirt with the image of the scar on it right across the abdomen (It's actually pretty cool—I have one at home). But not today.

They're milling around, craning their necks at the skylights or looking at details on the floor. I leave them there to decompress for a bit and find the guy who sat it out.

When I return, I am straight back into it.

'The next one is a bit of a walk to the South Wing, within a group of pieces that deal with the same theme.'

I give them the next spiel walking backwards. An artform in itself.

'Seeing all three of these works together at the same time is often overwhelming. The curator and designers have compartmentalised it, but it can still be a bit of a wild ride. Is everyone ready?'

Still keen, most of them nod. A few are unsure.

I march us through two large metal doors that swing outward.

The whole room is taken up with a stuffed, soft-foam forearm: hands rounded and chunky, as from a child's drawing of a hand. The wrist, like a fallen tree. It blocks most of the space. It is attached to the floor, which is decked in the pink polka-dot patterned flannelette of kid's pyjamas.

Sticking out of the wall to the right of the hand is a semi-flaccid penis that swings to and fro. A hydraulic system lifts the giant hand up to the penis.

'If you get sick of looking at it, you can squat down and the hand almost obscures the genitalia altogether.'

I don't say it very loud, because it seems disrespectful to the creator to actively deny or avoid the point of the piece. But there are only so many times I can look at a child's hand being made to touch what is clearly a grown man's penis.

But you know, the visitors love it. They're mildly shocked; ooh and tut every time.

Once enough of them have turned their backs or are standing closer to me, I project my voice again.

'This creation, dated 1983, is entitled Babysitter. It's the first in the series. The pieces are numbered 3, 4 and 5 in the book and 7, 8 and 9 on the audio guide.

'Before we continue, does anyone have any questions or comments?'

I need a distraction this time.

An old woman in designer drapery and expensive highlights asks:

'Is it intentional that you can only see the work from this side of the room?'

'Great question. Yes, it is. She is trying to recreate the feeling of being stuck and that the only thing moving is the hand being brought up to the phallus...'

I relish using words like genitalia and phallus when I talk about this work. They're such sanitised, art-world words. Sometimes I want to use the word dick or cock or even wiener, but it would make people laugh, which is gross.

We shuffle through the small doorway to the next work. It's down the end of a short, but wide corridor painted blue and they all talk amongst themselves. A couple of young women sidle up to me, hoping to chat, catalogue and notebooks out.

'Um, excuse me – in the guide, it mentions the floor and the space being decorated as bedclothes. We were wondering, was that, like, pyjamas or bed covers?'

'Both, actually. I think that's why that term was used –for ambiguity; to cover both definitions.'

They both scribble into their books and smile, grateful. I do love it when the nerds come in.

'It's worth mentioning that this next piece is being acquired by a public collection, so you may get to see it more often.'

I turn around and do the walking backwards thing again.

'So, how's everyone doing?'

People nod, ambivalent.

As they all shuffle in, the guy in the scarf waits again.

'You've seen this one too?'

He nods.

'And the next one?'

He nods again.

We exchange a knowing look. His, of shock. Mine of compassion.

I follow the rest of the group inside.

The room is darkened. Loud music plays. Coloured festoon lighting blinks on and off. There is a second soundtrack: a sporting event, crowds yelling occasionally. Azzaaaat! The smell of barbecue floats in, mixed with the smell of beer and cigarettes.

They all snoop around, drifting into corners and discovering different points of view, trying to make sense of it. Looking for a didactic panel, a clue. The ones with the catalogue always try to stand underneath the string of erratic bulbs, trying to look it up. Those who chose the audio version, stab at the player, trying to find an answer. All of them have the same confused expression on their faces.

I fuck with them even more by walking briskly through the work, as though it is a thoroughfare.

If I'm feeling sanctimonious, sometimes I don't even stop for questions there. Let them brood on it. Or not have any answers at all. Today, I don't know, I must be feeling OK.

'So, any—'

Six hands shoot up high. Like school.

'…questions?'

'What the fuck was that?'

Laughter clacks up and down the walls.

That is the artist's desired response. Confused horror.

'It's an ongoing piece – a performance work. After each showing, a new piece is added, although nothing has been added for at least six months. Like a Dan Graham work, there can often be a random performer in there.'

The rapture lady puts her hand up again. Properly this time. Bold.

'And the title?'

'That changes too, so some of you may have different titles in your notes. What are some you have?'

'Summer When I Was Eleven.'

'Dad.'

'A Treatise on the Place Between the Teeth and the Epiglottis.'

That's actually my favourite title.

'Let me see the most recent one…'

I fish out a folded piece of paper from my pocket.

I usually keep my hands free for these things. No notes. But I need this one because the bloody title is never the same and I can't remember it.

'The current title is: Retching Comes from Somewhere and from Somewhere it Comes, Retching.' I look up at them after saying that. Try to look them all in the eye. They don't even want to know why it was called other things. Sometimes at this point in the tour, I really do want them to ask. Because I'd want to know if an antagonistic gallery guide was hinting so strongly at me.

Scarf guy sneaks through on tiptoes to join us. I'm tempted to ask him a question, like 'why are you here if you keep skipping all the really distorted ones?' But I don't.

As we speed walk to the next display, he says to me, 'I saw the performer last time.'

'You did?'

'Yeah. A hairy guy in red speedos. Just runs at you out of nowhere. Scared the shit out of me.'

'Me too. So many times.'

We arrive at the final piece in this southern wing. There's a pretty standard warning sign on the wall near it, which they're all vaguely looking at when I catch up to them.

'In case any of you haven't read it yet, this work is also quite graphic. Namely, images of sexual violence with a minor. If you need to avoid it, let me know and I'll take you through the alternative route.'

Old mate in the Hermès raises his finger, like he's getting the bill. I nod discreetly and look around for anyone else.

Nope, all newbies. All think they are going to be enlightened by the contemporary art they're seeing. Good luck to them, I guess. They keep me in a job.

The low door slides open and most of them duck under and enter the room.

Before giving them the lecture, I open the side exit for the guy who's seen it before and assure him we won't be too long. Being so familiar with a visitor feels odd. And enjoyable. Like we're co-conspirators.

Before I start the work, I add a few extra details, to build tension.

'You'll see that the work is dated 1993–2001 and this is an edition, believe it or not.'

They look around the room and wonder how it could possibly be reproduced.

'Every few years, the artist builds an entirely new one. Rather than 'editions' she calls them a replay. Commissioned, they are installed in three or maybe four galleries around the world. Last year, all the galleries ran the works at the same time on a single day.'

No one ever cares about that bit.

'If you get disorientated, the exit will be behind you. Once the work has begun, that may feel confusing, but that's where the exit is.'

I flick the lights.

The room is highly reflective. In each panel, a large steak takes up the bottom half of the image. As each piece of mirror joins up and the floor sinks, the viewer will be surrounded and engulfed within that imagery. A middle-aged man fucks the piece of meat and his voice 'tell me you love me' blasts over the speakers. It's loud and repetitive and the lights flash through the mirrors.

The loop continues to play and I watch the visitors swiveling around for the exit. A young emo kid is the first one to remember my instructions and walks backwards. They bang into the lower step and start backing up. The rest follow suit, looking down on the image of the meat, which, as soon as there are people on the stairs, becomes a teenage girl.

A fuzzy brush, on pistons, brushes close to the audience's faces. At the top step, money rains down from the sky and the piece ends with the faint words of a girl's voice saying 'I love you'. The room goes black.

I stand at the one-way mirror window in the corridor watching them stumble out of the doorway. They do not like that one. It is pretty fucking awful.

'So we're over halfway. Shall we find the coffee shop?'

They're gasping for some relief, so we do it. Which is good, because it gives me time to check my messages and scroll through the timeline for a bit.

The bell tower above the front entrance chimes one, two, three. I look at my watch and see that, shit, I'm running late. See, this is what happens when you don't leave questions to the end. I've done it again.

I scoop up the group, but there's someone missing.

'She said she had to go,' one of them mumbles as I start counting heads.

'Oh, that's a shame. I hope she's ok.' Ha. Got one.

'Next stop, 2001.'

I don't know why I decided to do this chronologically—there's no fun, no wild history to concoct this way. Just 'this is the body of her work'.

I perform checking my watch and do a fake double take.

'I'm sorry, folks, but we're running a tad late, so I'm going to get through the next few quite quickly. I want to make sure there's time for your burning questions and some discussion at the end.'

Mostly nods. Almost everyone is still holding coffee. It's fine. If they spill it, it won't matter on the carpet.

'The North Wing is quite sparse, just a single work. There are plans to install her newest piece here... when it's finished.' I try to add a tone of intrigue and it comes out weirdly. Like a Halloween costume.

'Our offices are also in this section of the building, which makes this next work our least favourite, because it's a sound piece. It's number 14 in the book and 12 on audio.'

They scowl at the pages, and frown at the famous actor narrating, while I scoot us underneath the pale blue skylight. I look up at it every time and smile while they're not looking.

'As you'll see, it's called Wisdom. Teeth. Local. Nineteen. Ninety-Six. The title is a reference to age, the year it was made and the method of production. Local is a reference to both anaesthetic and site.

'It's quite a small room, so please shuffle in.'

They perch on the white enamel scoop seats that line the oval closet. There are 32 spots and only two spare by the time I squeeze in –one in front, which doesn't have a seat in it, and one behind, which does. I sit in it the space behind, sharp elbows dig in, knees touching. we can smell each other's breath.

I press the button.

The sound of breaking bones floods the small room, which is lined with large white fluffy cotton wool-type material. A soundtrack of muffled dialogue and the loop of bones being broken starts again.

Can't stay in that room very long. So claustrophobic, even after all this time. I *hup!* up out of my seat and we pile out, gasping for air. All our teeth on edge.

I walk us all briskly to the left, retreating past the ad billboard-style child death room. I'm tired of that piece. But the visitors croon their necks again to photograph themselves against the headlines: Don't Play in Boot – Father Warns. They do the smile she does in her headshot.

'As we come to this work in the West Wing, you'll see that it mirrors the one we saw earlier on in the East Wing.'

I point to the ceiling. Not because they'll understand, but it's a known thing to do when you're trying to talk about the structure of a place: look at the roofline.

'This section was remodelled to accommodate this particular work and to create a symmetry between the two pieces.'

My shoes clip-clop across the hard floor, tracking my movements like a radar. I disappear as I step down into the soft, carpeted floor of Radial Thredbo.

This is my favourite work. It's not necessarily the most interesting, but it's comforting to me. Of course it's because of the dark brown fluffy underfoot. The whole room is covered in the stuff. A bit like a Kathy Temin work, although never say that to the curator: they used to be friends.

'Please feel free to lie down on the carpet, or on the cushions.'

They've already done it, but I say it, just to be an arse – make them feel bad for doing it. I get a bit possessive over the works I like: afraid that if they like it too much, they might not want to leave. Or they won't try to understand it.

IMAX-esque, the viewing platform is halfway up the screen, at a keen angle, only obvious once the film starts. Makes my feet tingle.

There are two large, bent arms in sharp and clear focus across two video panels. Underneath is the faint suggestion of bike handles and moving ground underneath, the sound of breaking brush and bird calls: like a furry rollercoaster. The hypnotic ride is interrupted with a crack and a pitching forward of the camera, giving the viewers an even sharper angle, and an echo of what could be an animal crying out in the bush. At this point, the elbow of the right-hand arm detaches into a third video panel and takes a different journey: down a sharp incline, through brushland, hoisted onto the blurred suggestion of human shoulders, across a stream of a dark and rushing river in slow motion, into a car that stays stationery and then into a hospital room. Throughout this side journey, the left side of the piece is still moving up and down on a loop through the bush track of the initial rollercoaster ride, with the connecting angle of the arm missing. Both the two 'parts' of the film fade to black and join up again as crooked arms, the right in a sling, the left with the tattoo of a magpie.

When the video is done, we all leave the nice warm pussy room, as I affectionately call it. One of my colleagues calls it 'The Armpit', which is disgusting and very clever. I will never call it that. I like that artwork. I do not want to imagine myself in the crook of a hairy armpit when I'm on that ride.

'I see the similarities between the broken arm work,' one of the younger guys offers. Nice one, Sherlock.

I smile and nod.

'Even down to the brown of the chair in that one and the brown of the cushions in this one.'

OK, that's pretty astute.

'And the whole thrill of jumping up and down on a chair and then the intense bike ride,' offered another.

They were all talking like this —so excited to have discovered the clue I left them. But I liked this work, so I wasn't going to let them ruin it for me.

All teacherly, I wait for them to congregate in a small cove. Painted just-about-grey, a single spindly olive tree hovers next to me. It's the only living thing in here, really.

I cast my eye over them.

I love this part of the tour. They're all talking amongst themselves; all comfortable. Relaxed. About to be fucked up and they have no idea. I like to think the artist made it this way. Injure them and they become part of her work. That's how I'd do it.

'On the other side of these doors are two separate-but related works. I'm not sure if contemporary work like this would ever be classed as a diptych, although they do consist of large flat plates on hinges, reminiscent of the altarpieces of yesteryear.

'Called First Movement D (2002) and Second Movement C (2003-2019), which some of you may pick up—'

'—classical music.'

Did he just interrupt me?

'… is a classical music reference. But also political and medical references. The works are very loud: 160 decibels, which is the same as standing next to an amplifier in a rock concert. In a minute, I'll ask you to put on these industrial earmuffs before entering the gallery. Take a pair of clean ear covers, too.'

I gesture to the rack of earmuffs and a box of sanitary covers, like I'm on a game show.

They respond like seagulls to hot chips, barely performing politeness.

'Sorry'; '''scuse me'; 'oop'; 'I'll just...'

I stand on a step and survey them. They all look so cute with them on: like their heads have handles.

I put mine on and start the work, watching the large stainless steel doors gathering momentum. It's already loud, so I smile wanly and nod towards it.

I watch them disappear through the swinging doors, terrified, and whisper

'Any questions?'

A large door swings open inwards to an antechamber, which is centred by a black aperture doorway, opening and closing. As each viewer steps into the room, often having to squeeze through the rapidly closing hole, the sound of an industrial mega vacuum cleaner sucker (tuned to a D-minor) fills the dimly lit room. Over and over again. A low light swings back and forth, keeping time to the noise and the door mechanism. Only one viewer is allowed at a time and must continue on through the second set of swinging doors.

Large heavy swinging doors move like a pendulum, creating a sense of danger to the work. Audiences are met with a blast of discordant orchestral music, playing at a powerful 160db (the noise of a freight train). Each musical 'movement' is followed by a random sequence of piercing red lasers around the heated room. The intensity of the noise is painful and it is a relief to leave. The feeling of relief is the purpose of the work itself.

Epilogue

Last week the Gallery commissioned a surprise new work: Nude Clattering Down Staircase. Two big-ass paintings – a cross between the surrealist Man Ray work Bride Descending Stairs, all sharp angles and forward motion, and a Jenny Savage nude, all bumps and bruises and soft edges. It's not going in the North Wing, like the one I mentioned. This one will sit between the West Wing arm work and the doors to the southern section. They already sent out the press release, which of course started with 'We are pleased to announce…' Why are galleries pleased with such banal things? This new development means we will be closed for a while. And now I'll have to rewrite the whole guided tour.

CHRISTALIEN

NINA K. FELLOWS

In a painting from 1486 by Crivelli, *The Annunciation with Saint Emidius*, a long line of light leans down from the heavens to strike the forehead of the Virgin Mary. The light, which has the precision of a laser beam, slices through the scene from a vaguely circular form – a concentric lump of cloud, like an atomic bomb mid-detonation. Another devotional Renaissance painting of the Madonna and Child depicts a domed, stone-like object looming in the sky. A shepherd watches it fly, shielding his eyes. Certain fringe conspiracy theorists have identified these as the earliest recorded UFO sightings. Art historians argue that they're merely allegorical: the idea of a vortex of angels or the smooth face of God, the ineffable celestial, rendered two-dimensional for the mortals. But they are uncanny, aren't they? When humanity metabolises heaven, alienness seeps out.

When I found out I was pregnant, I acted fast. I calculated the date of conception, numbered the days, read some pamphlets, and booked a clinic appointment. There was never a question. What creator asks their progeny if they'd like to be? I had the clear focus of a fine tyrant – get it out, get it out, get rid. I wanted to finish my degree, write a book, travel the world and throw parties, not have a baby. Motherhood sounded to me like psychic death. My boyfriend was calm and saintly-patient, reminding me that this was entirely my choice. I had felt so light and in love, the two of us wrapped up in each other as often as possible, and my grip on my cycle had slipped a little. This was unfamiliar territory for me and my paranoiac tendency to withdraw. Our togetherness felt how I'd heard it was supposed to: honest and unguarded, terrifying, like finding yourself naked in the garden without so much as a fig leaf. I let myself relax; I stopped being careful.

After the first ultrasound, jelly smeared on my abdomen, I was told it was too early to confirm the pregnancy, so I'd have to wait two weeks. The initial realisation, my annunciation, hadn't been too awful. It was just a knot I needed to untie – until this two-week sentence proliferated knots along every sinew within me, a thousand bully ropes lashing me to my mistake. I was caught, arms tied at the elbows, my hands calcifying into claws, my spine twisted. Every meal I ate, I suspected slivers were being stolen from my plate to feed the greedy thing. I once told my mother I thought pregnancy was horrifying, a little parasite feeding on your body, distorting it, demanding you give your life for it. That's a terribly masculine fantasy, she told me, a sci-fi mythology dreamt up by boys afraid of women. She showed me a Polaroid my father had taken of her in her eighth month. She is naked, heavy-bellied, resplendent. Her Madonnaish resolve beams out of her and there ought to be trumpets and fat little cherubs hovering around her head. She willed me into being, fed me her body and her blood, and gave me this mad flesh-engine I was struggling to operate.

In Ridley Scott's *Prometheus*, the previously infertile Dr Elizabeth Shaw is impregnated by her alien-infected lover. She sprints down the clinical spaceship corridor to the med-pod, doubling over in pain, and smacks the buttons of the big machine. 'I NEED [gasp] CAESAREAN.' 'ERROR. THIS MED-POD IS CALIBRATED FOR MALE PATIENTS ONLY.' She presses more buttons. 'SURGERY – ABDOMINAL – PENETRATING INJURIES – FOREIGN BODY.' She climbs into the pod, morphine-loaded syringe between her teeth. Small mechanical hands appear – one scans her abdomen, another sprays her with iodine, and the third emits a cauterizing laser which slices her belly open. She screams at them to work faster and stabs herself with the syringe. Two delicate pincers reach into her and lift out an amniotic sac, swollen and black. The alien writhes and bursts it. The machine fires staples into her gaping wound and the grey, fishlike alien waggles its tentacles with naked aggression. Splattered with blood and sweat and iodine and amniotic fluid, Dr Shaw escapes the pod and locks the alien inside. She runs.

I became a scholar of abortifacients. I poured scalding-hot water over whole bunches of parsley, drank it, mouth burning, chewed the fibrous green into lumps and swallowed it. I emptied jars of powdered cinnamon into my tea and guzzled it, nose pinched, retching. I drank orange juice by the litre and tasted bile. I ate tinned pineapple until my lips and tongue felt like they were bleeding. I punched myself in the gut over and over again, hands balled into hard, fighting fists, boxing myself, beating it out. I read about pennyroyal, black cohosh, mugwort, tansy, ergot, rue. And I waited, Christ, how I waited. I was a hijacked plane, bastard gun in the cockpit, a long shrill squall ripping through the cabin and hurling me into freefall. I was convinced the little terrorist was sucking the life force out of me.

The horror of the alien is the lifeform you can't control, a dread life that finds you, worms its way into you and threatens to tear you apart. Life where life doesn't belong, rising up out of the barren seas of Mars, the lamella that refuses to die. A mute, brutal organism doing its nuclear wriggle across spacetime, belittling the Earth and debunking the myth of human exceptionalism. Language and reason dissolve in its slimy track.

When a woman finds herself alone on a spaceship, pursued by an eyeless, drooling alien, who does she pray to?

The wait for my abortion sent me stratospheric with an existential terror that tugged on every strand of my identity. Genetically, I am an (unbaptised, non-practising, ambivalently atheistic) Irish Catholic, on my mother's side. I was born guilty, full of shame at the fact of my being before I was old enough to do anything wrong. In the search for a salve for my inborn guilt, I look constantly upward for answers, craving ritual, instruction, and the promise of release. I am neurotic, fractious, fatalistic, perpetually awaiting an apocalypse that never happens. I can count on one hand the number of times I've been to mass, but I recite the Lord's Prayer when I'm frightened. My father's side of the family is from Yorkshire. His hometown was parochial, hemmed in by fields and churches, and he was from another planet, happier building Meccano robots than playing football. He must have seen the same twitchy, shrinking tendency in my kid-self, so to architect my wild imagination and gird it with the steel needed to withstand the hell of school, he gave me science fiction.

He explained to me rudimentary quantum physics, via Schrödinger's cat, when I was eight. He lent me books by J.G. Ballard, Robert Heinlein, Arthur C. Clarke, Michael Moorcock, steering me towards the tricky, trippy world of 'hard' sci-fi and postmodern speculative fiction. There are no gods in these universes – only the granular material of science, new substances and technologies, the dystopic human and eternal robotic. He inducted me into the Gigerian hall of machinery fused with flesh, where Alien's relentless pursuit of Ripley and Dr Shaw set the track for my trepidation. Her feet pound the metal floor of the interstellar corridor in a sprint for her life. She finds a weapon, makes a weapon, makes herself a weapon, ends up the only weapon alone on that ersatz comet, just her and the monster locked in an unending cosmic struggle. A woman defending her body like the last battleground in the solar system is the only worthy opponent for a parasitic monster looking for a host to burst.

Having been raised by a lapsed Catholic and a sci-fi geek, I'm a born sceptic, and I haven't yet met a sceptic whose pride in their rationality doesn't hide a desperate want for faith. I've sat in church, every muscle clenched as I tried to see whatever the congregation saw, and left with my miserably frustrated God-want still unfulfilled. I bet it was easier to feel shielded by some benevolent power before humanity broke through the clouds. Realising, as a species, that beyond our blue roof is an eternity of roiling black nothing studded with jagged rock and burning gas would surely make it hard to believe in the immutable kingdom of man. Nature cracks and splinters in the wide eye of outer space. Just imagining the nightmarish scale of the universe made my attempts at belief both impossible and imperative. My whole life, I wanted to feel placed within some cosmic order, to believe in an angelic hierarchy, but could never shake the sense of my body being nothing more than a lonely atom cast about upon an incalculable chaos.

During those two weeks in outer space, I was chased by hallucinatory visions of spiritual persecution. Godless me, seeing saints and martyrs stuck with arrows, bleeding, their skin peeled back, their eyes plucked out, their breasts cut off. Perhaps my lifelong yearning for God was a need for consequences – a certainty that the reckless things I'd done with my body would amount to something. I'd flayed myself, poisoned myself, threatened my own life, to no answer. Pain for the saints is an education, a making-oneself-a-vessel, a grand path, but so many things moved through me and went nowhere. I wanted salvation or condemnation, not this endless runoff, the outpouring of everything my body couldn't contain never reaching a conclusion.

The bitter irony of it: after years of introjected hate, I finally fell in love and was rewarded with the threat of a motherhood I didn't want. Why was my pleasure and never my pain *heard* by whoever doles out the consequences? By the end of those two weeks, I was haggard. I wondered if my ferocious shame would outlive the embryo. I got a second ultrasound and was awarded with a date for my abortion: August 24th. I saved it in my calendar as 'exorcism'.

The trouble with the death of God, so say theorists of theothanatology, is that humans must write the rulebook, and what a terrible burden it is to hold that pen. Nobody will punish our sins, so we must punish ourselves. Men of learning scratch their chins while us girls hammer out the equation. Bulging from my days in the teenage shame-trenches and my nights hungering for an organising principle, the psychic muscle that pulls bullshit dogma inwards started spasming in me like a steel piston. Think of the little babies, sweet fat cherubs, the tiny darlings you would frogmarch to the slaughterhouse clinic! Think of the essential nature of womanhood you'd deny, selfish cunt, taking it in and giving nothing back! I didn't believe this, did I?

I took a long drive with my best friend, the two of us in her car swinging wide through the dark night of the countryside, and I told her about the slick filth that covered me – every thought a sin, every step a sin. She was not shocked, and said, simply: that's it. That's womanhood – the guilt, the shame. It'll always come down to that, your constant apology for being.

My best friend is an actor, and she used to earn money doing medical roleplays. She would be given a script that personified a diagnosis, and medical students would have to question and diagnose her correctly to pass their exams. She once played a teenage girl who believed she was pregnant with an alien baby. I looked over her script, and the horror of the story hit a nerve in my gut. The psychiatric equation the script was meant to elicit – psychotic disorder plus possible sexual abuse equals delusion – felt insufficient. Her whole construction was cruel. This imaginary girl harbouring an alien embryo was created as a vessel for a clinical concept, her body made to be stretched out atop a slab of theory, awaiting the scalpels of smarter, saner people. She was the unwilling mother to a hypothetical problem, her narrative inhabiting the body of my best friend for the time it took some students to interrogate their way to the answer. A Martian blastocyst nestled in the belly of a Russian doll: fiction upon fiction, girl within girl, container-container.

The embryo is the size of a grain of rice. It has a primitive face with large, dark circles where the eyes will grow. The placenta sprouts out of the amniotic sac to feed nutrients from the host to the embryo. The neural tube forms. The ears appear as small flaps on either side of the head. Fingers and toes appear at the ends of small nubs that will become limbs. The head, which swells at the cranium and dwarfs the facial area, makes up one third of the total mass of the body. It hangs by a thread in the black space inside you, suspended like a bug in amber. It wiggles, but is too small for you to feel it moving. It has no sentience, no idea that it exists inside of you – no idea of you, no idea of itself.

It can't apologise, or forgive you, or stop sucking on the placental straw. It just *is*, and should it cease to be, it won't know about it. It doesn't know joy, and it doesn't know pain. It will disappear back into the blackness, soundless as a dying star, a distant speck that might have meant something to you if it hadn't been so small and far away.

Having railed at the speck, myself, and fate throughout my wait for the end, I ran out of anger as the bright exit of abortion came to meet me. By that point, I was feeling heavy and queasy, fogged up and slowed down by the tidal waves of hormones. In the last days of its mayfly life, I realised a compassion for the tiny animal inside me. The body I was furious with wasn't the one in my womb. Poor little bug, made of love – the love I'd made with my boyfriend, in all tenderness. We were just kids who made a bed warm enough for something to sprout from. Why the horror? Why was the radiant love of my own mother's motherhood so foreign to me? If I couldn't stretch my heart around this almost-baby, couldn't I at least make peace with myself? I hovered in the space between my rage and my forgiveness.

Deliverance came down the aisle swinging no censer, singing no hymns. My boyfriend came with me to the clinic, a small dark building sitting in a side alley. I filled out some forms and met a nurse who fed me the first pill and loaded me up with painkillers. They gave me the second pill, then we got a cab home and went straight to bed. I lay there, swaddled up to the neck, as an opiate fog crept up around me. Half-dozed and spaced-out, I waited, prone, with him beside me. The cramps started slowly. I felt the steady tension build, clench into pain, and fade. We watched a show about creepy tourist spots, the host treading nervously around nuclear wastelands with a ticking Geiger counter. Slow ticking – walk a few yards, faster ticking – faster and faster ticking, nervous glances – back away, slow ticking, slow. The tightening and release in my gut was picking up speed, and the apex of each cramp felt sharper than the last. I curled into the foetal position, shut my eyes, and let the pain drop me down through the centre of the Earth.

I was hanging in the blackness by a thread, hardly able to feel his hand stroking my hair. A slow spin outside of time, gigantic, planetary. I floated softly in a still, safe darkness, and then came the pain. A righteous, flaming spike punctured me and filled my closed eyes with startlingly bright flashes and pops of light, arresting everything – sight, thought, sound blasted clean away by a maddening arc of pain blazing up through my womb and out, enveloping me in its explosion. I saw burning balls of gas ten times the size of the sun moving unwitnessed in the dark. I felt meteors of rock and ice rip through my gut and shatter in my thighs. I was only a cold channel of gasping breath aerating an inferno. Then it disappeared, the light and fury gone, and I was back in that sweet amniotic sea. I hung there for a moment, blissful, and then it returned – the exploding chorus of atomic fireworks, the ecstatic agony again, and again, and again. The pain was a string of shooting stars, luminosity and blackness in sequence, and I rode every slash and blast of it. I was out there convulsing in a staggering eternity, alone inside my body, stabbing my flag into it. It was glorious.

I finally landed, finding myself back there on the bed. I was curled up tight and drenched in sweat, his hand still resting gently on my forehead. He helped me crawl upstairs to the bathroom. I sat on the toilet and the wreckage flooded out of me – blood and shit and sheer relief. Still bent double and in too much pain to swallow, I sucked water from a wet flannel. I laughed a mad laugh. I went back to bed and slept heavily. I cramped and bled some more, softer. That night we had steak. Into a sputtering hot pan I lay mine, a thick, fatty cut, just long enough for the edges to turn brown. I cut into it, still bleeding, and it melted in my mouth like butter. I was feeding myself, only myself.

For months after the abortion, I often dreamt I'd had a son. He was a dark-haired, stern-faced little boy. He looked sombre and dressed very smartly, like he was going to a funeral. I didn't resent him. He had made me a mother, and by extent a dutiful wife, and I walked around a hospital in long skirts with his austere, quiet patter constantly at my side. We were companions: a good boy and a good woman. He looked the spit of Damien from the Omen, I thought each time I awoke, but back there in the dream-space, he wasn't evil. He was sweet, benign, my little bug.

I think the boy appeared to reassure me – of what, I don't know. Perhaps that he'd be waiting for me on the other side of life, for when I was ready to recreate him. Or that, had I been forced to let him grow, I would have handled it the best I could. He would have been a nice, polite, well-turned-out boy, like the sons of so many mothers who didn't get to choose. He wouldn't be a vessel for my shame, forever carrying some blot like I thought I would be. If I'd had him, I'd recognise myself in the jut of his nose or see my boyfriend in his blue eyes. He wouldn't be alien to me. I needed the spectre of him, I think, to prove it.

In my rage and fear, the abortion took on the contours of a different kind of emptying-out. I have such deep respect for those who have to wade through conservative bureaucracy, misogyny, and religious condemnation to access safe abortions. I was so lucky, so stupidly privileged to only have to fight myself, so why did I invent reproach where none presented itself before me? I was given a clear path to escape, and I cluttered it with my hand-wringing. My hyperactive guilt made it harder than it needed to be, true – but that particular guilt, the indictment of female self-interest, is an implantation. I was harbouring a fugitive diktat, a disgust with my own anatomy and reckless want, that had lain dormant in me long before I saw it. That August day I spent stuffed with pills and bleeding like a broken faucet was a necessary reckoning. I was digging up the deep seed of original sin, renegotiating a contract with my own flesh.

I stared down that long beam of light compelling me to make myself a vessel for a fresh, clean little life, to make myself a mother of consequence, and denied it. Defending my own mess of an existence by refusing to give up my ambitions and pleasures in service of an infant felt like defying nature itself. Humanity, in science fiction, is bizarrely self-justifying; it simply *must* continue to perpetuate itself, to conquer and colonise and procreate, even in dystopic futures and on barren planets where survival seems not just improbable but unwise. The alien that refuses to die is a mirror of that maniacal life-instinct, our psychic parallel represented as monstrous.

Wrestling with my body's reproductive urge, watching it go for the throat of all my hopes, alienated me from my own flesh. Deciding to abort and knowing that some would consider me a murderer made me an alien, too – alien to an ancient dogma that would throttle bodily autonomy to save the sanctity of an unrealised potential future, alien to a salvation I still want to believe in but won't be welcomed into until I consider my sex and self-preservation sinful. I will not apologise my way to absolution. If alienness is contravention of the laws of man and nature, ceaseless life, defiant, hungry life, then I am alien, hanging out there in the darkness amongst the burning stars. But I am, I suspect, only human.

PHANTASMAGORIA

ABI HYNES

Phantasmagoria: *a sequence of real or imaginary images like those seen in a dream.*

We spent half an hour trying to 'thread the needle'. You sit on the floor, plant one foot and lift the other. You clasp your hands, and as you try to stand (one-legged, remember, like a heron) you *thread the needle* of your lifted leg through the eye of your arms. Then back down again, each movement in reverse. It was the sort of torture-disguised-as-training that our physical theatre teacher enjoyed. She liked to demonstrate, at length, and then watch us fail, marking against our names on her clipboard when we did. I had the sort of swollen, second-year-of-uni body you see worn by girls who didn't go to private school and are spending their own money for the first time – on beer and chips to fill the space inside them which has recently become huge and lonely. It was a body that had always wanted to move, but it had been through enough high school PE lessons and village hall ballet classes to know that it would only be punished for it.

Our university's music and drama building had been two blocks, once. At some point during modernisation they had been joined together but the floors didn't quite match up, which meant bizarrely sloping corridors and a fourth floor which, without the aid of a lift or a staircase, became the fifth, but only if you walked the length of it from one direction. There was a studio there that I could only sometimes find, with mirrored walls and a sprung floor that the suited classical musicians and the heavily made-up drama queens of my cohort had little use for. Usually, the blacks were drawn across the mirrors to make the windowless, low-ceilinged space feel even darker and more airless, so that standing alone in it meant trying to breathe as though with a hand over your mouth.

Phantasmagorical: *having the appearance of an optical illusion, especially one produced by a magic lantern. Changing or shifting, as a scene made up of many elements.*

The physical theatre teacher's name was Cassie. She had a severe haircut that should have been comic, but wasn't, and she was particularly fond of teaching us about what she called 'the cruelty of clowning'. She liked to get us up on stage, one at a time, in silence and with no instructions, to an audience of our classmates who were told to raise their hands as soon as they were bored. 'This is nothing,' she would tell us, if we looked hurt or angry. 'If you'd gone to drama school, you'd have to do this every day.' In warmups, she would get us to stand in a circle, arms windmilling, chanting, 'I've been to Lecoq!', which she had, but only for one summer. In our second class with her, we had to take turns to be dogs on leashes, while she gave us points on her clipboard for barking at birds, sniffing each other's arses, and pissing up against trees. At that point, one red-haired girl I'd always thought was rather sour walked out and didn't come back. I had a newfound respect for her after that.

Because most people had forgotten it existed, I found that I could block-book Studio 5 for most of the semester. I drew back the heavy black curtains to reveal the mirrors and wrestled two chairs from the complicated jungle of stage scaffolding behind the jammed partition. I found some heavy blue gym mats against the wall and laid them out to practice forward and backward rolls, always heaving them upright again before I left in case the cleaners complained. I guessed and strained my way through a series of half-remembered stretches I'd never have attempted if anyone else could have witnessed them. There were only three bands that I loved, and their songs reminded me of home too painfully, so though I often brought speakers and a laptop with me and set my girlfriend's iTunes on shuffle, it was more of a nuisance than an inspiration. And all the time I watched myself in those mirrors in a way I never had before. I watched like Cassie watched – like I was a stranger in the audience who didn't know myself.

Phantasmagoria (also fantasmagorie, fantasmagoria) *was a form of horror theatre that (among other techniques) used magic lanterns to project frightening images such as skeletons, demons and ghosts onto walls, smoke, or semi-transparent screens. In many shows, the use of spooky decoration, total darkness, (auto-)suggestive verbal presentation, and sound effects were also key elements. Some shows added all kinds of sensory stimulation, including smells and electric shocks. Even required fasting, fatigue (late shows) and drugs have been cited as methods of making sure spectators would be more convinced by what they saw.*

I knew I'd never be a dancer (I'd left it too late, I was too fat, I'd never have been fit enough), but I still wanted to be an actor, so I auditioned for the Drama Society plays in my first year at university. The older students liked to put you off while you waited in the corridor to be called, telling you how the director was dating one of their housemates, or recounting horror stories of past auditions when they'd had to play single cell organisms gradually evolving, and had been encouraged to writhe on the floor and 'mate' with each other. I spent one particularly gruelling afternoon repeating a monologue by a second-year about putting a tea bag inside my knickers, playing opposite a line-up of increasingly Dorito-flavoured boys because the other girls going for the role had been at a party the night before and were too hungover to show up. I didn't get that part; the writer had *wanted* to give it to me, she assured me, but the director had already promised it to one of her hungover friends (the director had been at the same party, and hadn't turned up to my audition, either).

Phantasmagoria *is a point-and-click adventure horror video game designed by* **Roberta Williams** *for MS-DOS and Microsoft Windows and released by Sierra On-Line on 24th August, 1995. It was made at the peak of popularity for interactive movie games and features live-action actors and footage, both during cinematic scenes and within the three-dimensionally rendered environments of the game itself. It was noted for its violence and sexual content.*

Three years after *Phantasmagoria* came out, and only two years after my family bought a home computer, my little sister and I discovered the multi-disk game on one of our parents' bookshelves. I was nine, and Susi was six. On investigation, we were told it was an 18 and inappropriate for children. So we played it secretly.

In the game, successful mystery novelist Adrienne Delaney and her photographer husband Don Gordon have just purchased a remote mansion previously owned by a famous 19th-century magician, Zoltan 'Carno' Carnovasch, whose five wives all died mysteriously. Adrienne, who had hoped to find inspiration for her next novel in her new home, starts having graphic nightmares as soon as they move in, and is comforted by the loving and supportive Don.

While exploring the grounds, Adrienne finds a secret chapel hidden behind a bricked-up fireplace. She opens a locked box that lies in waiting on the altar, and accidentally releases the evil demon that forced Carno to murder his wives. The demon possesses Don, who starts acting menacingly towards Adrienne, and rapes her.

Through a series of visions, Adrienne learns the various gruesome ways in which Carno slaughtered his spouses. Hortencia, who avoided his abuse by secluding herself in her greenhouse, is stabbed with gardening tools and suffocated with mulch. Alcoholic Victoria gets into an argument with Carno, who impales her with a wine bottle through the eye. An overly talkative third wife, Leonora, has her mouth gagged and her neck twisted 360 degrees by a torture device. And the food-loving Regina is force-fed animal entrails through a funnel until she chokes to death.

Reading the synopsis on Wikipedia, I find I can replay each of these scenes clearly in my mind. Once you reached each point of discovery, the game would trigger a three-minute video that couldn't be stopped, paused, or skipped once it had started. Susi and I could, of course, have left the room, but that option never seems to have occurred to us.

The Wikipedia synopsis states that the story ends when Adrienne successfully expels the demon from her husband, and escapes from its resulting fury long enough to perform a ritual that traps it once again inside the hidden chapel. I have no memory of that ending, because Susi and I never won the game. The ending I remember is round after round of being chased through the house by the still-possessed Don, who kills Adrienne in a different way depending on which room of the house he catches her in: the greenhouse (a trowel of dirt forced down her convulsing throat), the hallways (wine bottle through the bursting eye), the kitchen (glistening animal entrails, the practical shape of that funnel). The end we dreaded most of all came if he caught her in the chapel itself, trying uselessly to click on items that might let us perform the exorcism. Here, he would strap her into a chair disguised as a conjurer's machine and turn the handle that brought a guillotine-like blade down sideways through the centre of her skull, splitting it open and showing us the meat inside.

I have searched online, but I can't find a description of this ending anywhere.

Étienne-Gaspard 'Robertson' Robert, *was the most famous phantasmagoria showman – a Belgian inventor and physicist from Liège. He would often eliminate all sources of light during his shows in order to cast the audience into total darkness for several minutes at a time. Robertson would also lock the doors to the theatre so that no audience member could exit the show once it had started.*

Robertson sited his entertainment in the abandoned cloisters kitchen of a Capuchin convent (which he decorated to resemble a subterranean chapel) near the Place Vendôme. One of his first phantasmagoria shows displayed a lightning-filled sky with both ghosts and skeletons receding and approaching the audience. To add to the horrors he projected onto smoke and screens, Robertson and his assistants would sometimes create voices for the phantoms. Often, the audience forgot that these were tricks and were completely terrified. In fact, many people were so convinced of the reality of his shows that police temporarily halted the proceedings, believing that Robertson had the power to bring Louis XVI back to life.

When I spotted a callout for an independent production, advertised as a physical theatre project of the kind that nobody in the straight-laced Drama Society usually went anywhere near,

I couldn't resist. The director, who we'll call Matthew (he's a literary manager at a major theatre now, according to LinkedIn), was a third-year with plans to start his own theatre company, named for the length of time it took him to travel from his parents' London house to his university accommodation. I liked Ella, his producer, more than I liked him, but his avant-garde tastes and his 'not-fitting-in-the-boxness' spoke to me. The show was his own adaptation of *The Yellow Wallpaper*, and he and Ella had persuaded the Manchester Museum to agree to let them stage it in some of their unused attics.

I don't remember what I did in the audition, but I was unreasonably thrilled when Matthew called to tell me he was casting me as 'the woman in the wallpaper': a part that, admittedly, had no lines, but did require a physical performance that sounded pleasingly glamorous.

The Yellow Wallpaper *is a gothic short story by American writer Charlotte Perkins Gilman, first published in January 1892. A young woman and her physician husband rent an old mansion for the summer. To help her recover from her 'hysterical tendencies' after the birth of their first baby, he confines her to the nursery and forbids her to read or work. During her imprisonment, she imagines she sees a woman trapped within the room's yellow wallpaper, with whom she eventually trades places, or goes mad, depending on your point of view.*

You know what's coming. The reality was not quite what I'd pictured when I'd gleefully accepted the role. This was first heralded by Lola – a girl on most of my courses who regularly got drunk and told me I was beautiful so effusively that it made me suspicious of her motives. She sat down next to me at the start of our Theatres of the Middle East seminar and announced that she had been cast in the play she knew we'd both auditioned for: as the woman in the wallpaper.

It turned out there were three of us. I tried not to let the fact that I was sharing the role knock the shine off it too much, and in fact Lola, Hannah and I became friends. In rehearsals, we were united in our resentment towards the much posher and (in our view) significantly less talented India, who had all the lines and who Matthew had started referring to as his 'muse'. We, meanwhile, wriggled and writhed on against the walls on cue, occasionally adding in some spooky whispering, stopping only to be corrected by Matthew if he caught our octopus arms tiring and straying too close to the floor. ('It's the yellow *wallpaper*, ladies, not the yellow carpet!')

It had been made clear to us from the offset that our costumes were going to take the form of yellow leotards. When we were presented with them, they turned out to be made entirely of transparent, stretchy lace, and the shawls and gowns we had been told we would wear over them had been scrapped because Matthew didn't think they looked right. We were in the basement of his student house, which had been chosen for this pre-production costume fitting and photoshoot because of its appropriate grimness. The three of us stripped off, and I tried to brazen my way through the embarrassment of my childish bright purple underwear while Ella fiddled with the lamps and Matthew's camera clicked. We all laughed at how dodgy this would be – a director luring us to his basement to take photos of us barely clothed – if Matthew weren't gay. Ella's laugh was a little strained, I thought, but perhaps I've misremembered that.

At the time, my primary worry was that I was the largest of the three wallpaper women, and I sucked my stomach in so tightly during the costume fitting that I ached afterwards. Looking back at photos now, of course, I was lovely in the ordinary way that all 19-year-olds are lovely; soft, with rounded edges and a bad fringe that made me look even younger than I was. There was no talent or skill in my performance. Matthew wasn't interested in choreographing anything but the basic blocking that affected India, so we made up our wiggles afresh every night, and often missed our cues. But the overall effect, I'm told, was good – we were stationed behind gauze screens that hid us from the audience until the back lights blazed, and we could travel through and amongst them in the dark. And there had been a few points during rehearsals when it had seemed we might be onto something, when the excitement of discovery that was in the mind but also in the body had me tingling from head to foot. We were working on the end sequence, when the women burst out of the wallpaper at last and helped India to hang her husband, and the ideas were flowing freely between us. We tried a solution, which presented a new idea, which gave way to another, and I put forward a suggestion for the final moments of the show that we all knew was right. Perhaps I'd gone too far, though, because Matthew looked me straight in the eye.

'Do *you* want to direct the play?', he asked me, and I shut my mouth.

The best thing about that part in *The Yellow Wallpaper* by far was the shedding of some of my self-consciousness in that bizarre, revealing costume. In the last days of dress rehearsals, up in the museum attics, we three lace-clad women drifted about the building like yellow-stained ghosts. We took photos of each other in various contorted positions, marvelling at our creepy/sexy limbs, all tangled up together. Matthew had mostly lost interest in what we looked like, so we undertook various unsanctioned makeup tests, settling on a gold shimmer that we rubbed all over our arms and faces. We ate our lunch on the staircase, not caring how many baffled curators walked past.

The **Theatre of Cruelty (Théâtre de la Cruauté)** *is a form of theatre generally associated with Antonin Artaud. It has been described as a break from traditional Western theatre and a means by which artists assault the senses of the audience. Artaud's works have been highly influential on artists including Jean Genet and Peter Brook.*

Artaud wanted to abolish the stage and auditorium, and to do away with sets and props and masks. He envisioned the performance space as an empty room with the audience seated in the centre and the actors performing all around them. The stage effects included overwhelming sounds and bright lights in order to stun the audience's sensibilities and completely immerse them in the theatrical experience. Artaud believed that he could erode an audience's resistance by using these methods "addressed first of all to the senses rather than the mind'.

In our last ever class with Cassie, she put us into pairs. I worked with Asha, one of the only two brown-skinned girls on my course, and we were instructed to observe and then mimic each other: first standing, then walking. Cassie split the group in half, so that I sat in the stalls and watched as Asha did her Abi-walk around and around the stage, weaving in between the other mimicking students – all trying to be careful, still, at that point. Trying not to hurt anybody's feelings.

'Bigger!' Cassie called to them. 'Show me everything ten times bigger!'

Asha winced. She leaned back slightly and pushed her stomach – my stomach – forward. My face felt very hot, and I could smell the bitter tang of fear rising underneath my t-shirt. Cassie hovered at the edge of the performance space, her expression eager. *This is nothing! If you'd gone to drama school…*

'*Bigger!*' she shouted, walking amongst the students now, marking her clipboard with her hard, staccato ticks. 'Come *on* now, I want to see it from space!'

Asha let her stomach yawn forwards like a pregnancy. She waddled, pigeon-toed, and swung her arms vigorously, mannishly, at her sides. She tucked her chin so that the skin of her neck gathered in rolls, her crotch leading her back and forth and back and forth. There was no laughter in the room as I remember it. The performances were grotesque, obscene, completely ridiculous by the time that Cassie was satisfied with them, but those of us watching also knew that they were true. Most of us left the workshop that afternoon in silence, and when I got back to our flat I got straight into the shower, where I hated every inch of my own flesh so violently it felt like a promise, or a spell. I stayed there for a long time, and my skin burned and burned with shame.

In his lifetime, Artaud only produced one play that put the theories of the Theatre of Cruelty into practice. He staged and directed Leo Cenci, *adapted from the dramatic work of the same title by Percy Bysshe Shelley, in 1935 at the Théâtre des Folles-Wagram in Paris. The play was neither a commercial or critical success and ran for only 17 performances.*

The Yellow Wallpaper was the first and the only play that I was cast in at university. Too afraid of humiliation to keep auditioning, my girlfriend and I started producing our own shows, which I acted in at first but then, realising I was often the least talented performer in the room, soon stopped. We raided the drama department's costume store, a musty-smelling warren full of clothes donated by various local theatres, in which all the women's clothes were tiny and the men's were huge, like the way characters are drawn in Disney films or superhero comics. I abandoned my body to do as little as it wanted, and tried instead directing, and then writing. I was homesick for a home that had vanished when I left it; I was hungry and empty all the time, and never satisfied. If a bad photo sent me spiralling into self-hatred and despair, I would spend a few weeks starving myself and swimming lengths between lectures, or drag myself to ballet classes at the Dance House that made me feel like an idiot for ever imagining that I could move, let alone that anyone might like to watch me.

But I continued to choreograph dances and movement sequences for our little company's productions, and often only for myself, returning to Studio 5 to work for long hours alone right up until I graduated. I scribbled them down in notebooks in my own form of clumsy dance notation, but mostly I relied on the memory of my body, which clung to whatever felt good and seemed to tell the truth of something inside me that couldn't find expression any other way. Where Cassie's classes had punished me for showing up, my private hours in Studio 5 were nourishing in a way that I couldn't have explained to anyone. The scenes I created there were wordless, and often violent. I presented back to myself the shapes that women's bodies made in the films and plays I studied, and the shapes I had seen them make long before I arrived at university. The results were naïve and earnest and troubling. I'd had no formal training beyond what we did with Cassie and it showed. I had thought that getting a degree and studying the thing I wanted to do would be enough, but of course it wasn't. It took several tutors over several years (for I invited them to my plays even after I'd left) to hint, gently and not so gently, that I was kidding myself before the message really sunk in. I let the creature I had spied in the mirrors behind those black studio curtains (who was cruel as often as she was kind, who was me and not me) drift into the past tense. When she returned to me in the dark – distorted, improbable, phantasmagorical – I blinked until she faded into the walls.

Theory: *every story about a woman's body is a horror story.*

In our final year, I saw Lola in a production of *Les Enfants Terribles*, co-directed by Hannah and another friend of ours. She was excellent in it, much better than the girl who won 'best actress' at the student theatre festival awards that year. But she gave up acting altogether, then – a self-flagellating move I understood completely. Another friend I did my master's with went off to drama school after we graduated the way I'd always planned to – and sent back horror stories worse than anything Cassie had inflicted on us. A few years ago, Cassie's husband died suddenly, leaving her and her two young daughters devastated – I saw it on Facebook. These days we have some mutual friends, and I've seen her sometimes, at the bar before a show or waiting to pitch for the same small pots of local arts funding. I've changed her name in case she ever reads this and recognises herself, and thinks I've been unkind.

I have seen my own ghost many times since university. She still visits; I see her face beneath my face, her sharp teeth inside my mouth. She likes to surprise me in the bathroom at house parties; she can move where she likes, you see, insubstantial as she is, projected onto smoke. She presents herself, maimed and rotting, in my nightmares. Sometimes, for months, or even years at a time, I will be afraid to look at photographs of myself, knowing that she'll appear in half of them – disguising nothing, revealing me to everyone.

SUBNIVAL,
OR:
SISTER, TEACH ME
ABOUT TIME!

MARION MICHELL

m.e. is like a burglar who steals from you every minute of every day. its booty is your energy, half a sackful of cognitive functions, and whatever else it can find.

somewhere in-between. things hovering on a margin, a brink, about to fall. the artist tries to squeeze time into a photograph. not just a moment, but a passage. she photographs herself swaying: limbs dissolve in a flutter, her mouth disintegrates, she splits in two and two again, into ever fainter copies of herself.

she tries to arrest movement in film. halt the passage of time, extend moments at her will. while the camera skims his face. K sits motionless, his breath flat. when she checks the footage later, she finds a full minute of well-nigh stillness. she will edit out the blinks, produce a loop with a continuous, seamless stare.

out goes your profession, your social life; your mobility, vision, memory; your ability to look after yourself without help; your idiosyncratic vitality – in short: the way you were in the world. hardest though: your intelligence curls up in a ball and rolls out of reach and you lie in wait for those rare instants when you can seize it by the scruff of its scrawny neck and pull it from under the bed, for a wee while.

words are the flimsy hooks i sink into industry. i most fervently want to write when fatigue crashes down like a tidal wave, primal as a sea god's wrath, and my soggy self swirls off with shoals of plastic-bellied fish. when speech runs out completely; when eyesight gets so vague that the parakeets outside my bedroom window look like lime-green smudges; when turning over, even breathing is a chore; and sounds issuing from the radio (normally the last resort) feel like gristly morsels wedged in my throat. when i resurface selfhood is as insubstantial as a dust bunny. but there's a place in me where something stirs, and all i want is to reach – through layers of weariness – and let a string of words swim up from its sediment.

she hoards hush like treasure. her tongue lies heavy, snoozling in its lair, stirring when thoughts thicken. sister of swans – pledging silence she rhymes her name with naught.

casualties haunt: plans abandoned, fortunes ousted, friendships lost, lovers never met – gaunt-faced spectres eating the dust your tired in-house strides stir up. how do you envision a meaningful future, how do you connect, engage, keep learning, when cognition is beleaguered, and all you manage is minute-work?

she sits in the editing suite for hours, trying not to blink lest she miss the flap of lashes. one by one she clips them from the video. slowed down, and up close, they look like the synchronised wingbeat of a pair of pinned beasties.

*

every so often, for a short, giddy while, energy allows you to gather yourself, and fatigue is no more than a background hum. you sit, chat, smile, not thinking 'after', or 'before'. it's like standing at the top of a ladder that juts a little way beyond the edges of a steep ravine, shouting 'i contain multitudes!' (even remembering who said it first). subsequent days would be spent keening, were it not that thought and feeling require a degree of vitality.

desire and capacity grow at wildly disproportionate rates; frustration keeps a tally. half of me would like to lock the door, hole up with comrade sleep until i'm sure she'll never leave; the other half is raring to go. i want to be an explorer! a space traveller! a deep-sea diver! the captain of a steamship, a story-teller, a bird, a sea-anemone, a witch, a wild thing, a piece of rock on the moon, a ray of sun. in the meantime i praise myself for every little thing i do, incl. schlepping to the loo, ever slower as the clock ticks on. 'well done,' i say, trudging back with a racing heart. 'well done!'

a girl sits in a tree in the forest. wordless she hurls her love against the spell's wall, stitching blossom to blossom, year to year. did she eat? did she drink? did she get down the tree to pee? did she wash? did the flowers not wilt? was she afraid? was she cold? did it snow?

it is hard at times to feel oneself as more than a body in crisis, and, thanks to society's 'hostile environment', a body under harmful scrutiny. failure to perform, to work, to earn, is writ large. debilitating symptoms are judged deficiencies. how we pulse with life, desire, and creative passions, even when we lie at home, eyes closed, and, yes, requiring help with baths, meals, toilet needs, doesn't much signify in the outside world. we're not seen, rarely heard.

*

a famished eye trawls scripts and scrawls, in the tapered shapes of petals, a tendril's coil, the curl of a fern leaf. words flicker, cling and claw: fern, fernery, fernyear.

some days the phrase 'you're just not good enough' is all pervasive. it's the shape accrued frustration takes, a crust, or coat, too tight to wriggle out of. doubt thrives on silence (the chronic, polyester kind): your art, your writing; your sleep, your rising; your ability to liaise, converse, consider; your quests for energy and cure; upswing of any sort – whatever you try is veined with lack.

six shirts fit one into the other like russian dolls. the youngest brother, closest in age, the one she loved best - his shirt she kept for last, when it was hardest, her heart brimming. as time ran out a sleeve remained undone, and when he shed his plumed skin a wing sprang instead of an arm.

imagine a monitor suspended from the ceiling. you look down at the screen as if into a pond. at first glance the upturned face seems lifeless, as in a photograph. don't turn away! by and by the slightest movement of the head, a subtle swallowing motion, a twitch in one eye, become events.

as capacity and vision wane, i find in artistry the last unlittered chamber in the house m.e. built, where illness hollers curses through the door, but cannot rule.

i saw them once, on hampstead heath, blinking in the blinding sun, his wing around her shoulders white as light itself.

i gaze at the cursor on my screen. when i stay still it winks at me.

UNDERLAND

LOUISE KENWARD

One day I stopped.

Everything about me stopped. As if I had died but had forgotten to finish the job, it lacked commitment. I spent weeks, then months, in bed: a half-hearted end. I was frozen, suspended in aspic, undead.

I began to tell stories.

We have always told stories: it may be the one thing at our core. Writing stories is as essential to life as eating and breathing. Stories pass on words of caution or hope, messages from the past to the future. There are times it has felt as though my story was all I had, the most important part of being human, of being sick. It was important to get my story right. My story seemed to have none of the things a story needed; no beginning or end, no message or moral, no answer or hope. Alice was the only person who made sense: her adventures after rabbits and through looking glasses.

I had fallen down the rabbit hole.

I was squeezing through doors I didn't fit in, chasing rabbits with pocket watches and medical certificates. I was playing games with cards that got up and walked off from the table.

This was not Wonderland. This was my reality: living with a mysterious illness that no one could see. If it couldn't be seen, it couldn't be measured – and if it couldn't be seen or measured, then it couldn't be treated. If it couldn't be seen, it couldn't be true. Unless you're Alice, I decided. I must be Alice.

There were many Alices like me, all chasing white rabbits and drinking tea with the Hatter, hearing the voice of the Lobster in the distance. We were all trying to write our stories. Writing and talking, in the hope that our words would be heard, that we would be understood.

I started reading other people's stories – tales of hysteria, of fear and anger – of illness stretching years and lifetimes, tales of no return.

They gave me nightmares.

Other people had stories like mine, incomplete and insubstantial. The endings were not fairytale ones. I began to fear the story more than the illness itself.

Other people began to make up stories for me. My GP thought I'd had a virus, one I was taking too long to recover from. He couldn't tell me why that might be. Everything was normal. Nothing was normal. He couldn't be sure it was even a virus, it was one that skips about, can't always be seen, one that everyone has.

My mum thought I was burnt out: an old car on bricks, my insides hollowed, surface insubstantial, crumbly, flaking, blackened with charcoal.

In time, I got better without a story, but then it came back and demanded to be written.

Are there stories for things we don't know? Perhaps there are too many, or just the wrong ones. When our lives, our bodies, do not follow the rhythm of a story – when there is no elixir to be found, no charm to carry or spell to be cast. I am still lost in the woods with a witch.

Am I the witch?

I am in a tale where I am no longer the hero of my own story, I am playing a bit part – a side character, an incidental – without lines or character arc, there is no development, nothing moves on or gets resolved. I have walked into a book where the hero blocks my path and benign creatures turn into dragons. Those who might otherwise support me run for the hills, leaving poison apples in their wake – each with the power to send me to sleep for a hundred years. There is no name for this place I have fallen into, and perhaps that would help, to have a name – I could mark it on the map, plot grid references. This is an in between space. I'm at the edge, in the middle, underneath. I'm in a place where people can see me but they don't look, can hear me but they don't listen, and this goes on for so long all that's left of me is a trace of something suspended, hovering – like the grin of the Cheshire cat floating in the trees.

I am Alice. It is the only thing that makes sense. I am searching for Absolem, the Caterpillar on his mushroom, smoking from a hookah pipe. Everything is front to back and downside up and I have the validation of the white roses being painted red. Nothing to see here, as the packs of cards cover the white flowers in red paint, suffocating us and denying our reality: the greenfly, the rot, the infestations and damaged stems cannot be seen, covered in paint. But the more you protest that you are not a red rose, the greater your red rose status becomes. Suggested treatments are made for your denial of your redness. Interventions to change your unhelpful beliefs, to help you realise you are not a white rose. You are prescribed exercise for your denial of your rootedness to the spot – you are not unable to walk because you have no legs – limbs buried in the ground, weighted under earth – you are unable to walk because you aren't walking.

My story is still playing out. It's a horror story, a mystery, a fantasy, a betrayal. It's a story of pain and absence, of fearing I have entirely lost touch with reality. It is an incomplete story, but what there is, is entirely true.

One day I stopped. I am still unsure if this is the beginning or the ending. Perhaps it is the middle? It is unsatisfactory as a story, it is unsatisfactory as a life. But perhaps I can borrow other stories to fill in the gaps of my own.

One day I stopped.

Perhaps my disappearance is through my own negligence, my lax accounting for my body, it wandered off through disinterest or lack of attention. Perhaps it is no longer filled with blood and muscle, no internal organs for tests to show anomalies. Instead it is a building site, with scaffolding needed to hold up the foundations, unset concrete filling the walls. I've got bent out of shape as I bow and sag. There is no space to breathe, no air bricks installed, no windows to open. Perhaps I am a crab, in need of an exoskeleton, one that has moulted its shell, staggering about on the beach, hiding under rocks. I'm leaden, immobile, concrete set, shell outgrown. Part amoeba, part xylophone.

I am the dormouse in the teapot, the baby that turns into a pig. Nothing looks out of place, until you step inside. There are well meaning men, identical to each other (white coat, stethoscope), all pointing in different directions of which way I should go – all pointing in the wrong direction – not because they mean to, not because they are mean, they simply want to help. And they have no idea how.

It becomes folklore, a tale told of warning to others: don't follow that path, don't drink that potion! But the paths are overgrown, the signs are too hard to read. Potions look and taste the same. I am playing card games with no rules and croquet with flamingos. Myths and fragments of knowledge are passed on, through family and friends, between others who stopped. But when you are stopped, totally stopped, there are times when you are unable even to speak.

How can we tell our stories if we cannot speak?

'This is clearly a red rose,' they write.

The garden is overseen by the Red Queen, with the loudest and most piercing voice – it is hard to block out and continues to ring long after her call about roses has been made – it continues to resonate on the radio and in the papers. More packs of cards hear her cries and gather to find more efficient ways to paint the roses, for they must all be painted.

Chess pieces all come to life, obstructing routes to hoped for answers. There are Jacks and Jills falling down hills all across the land. The Hatter is in charge, or is your ally, or is a red herring – along with the roses. And no one knows what to do, so once the tea things are all used up, we just move on to the next setting and pour another cup. And the white rabbit with his pocket watch rushes by, always out of reach, only seen out of the corner of your eye. Skipping through bushes and underneath hedges, and you wonder if perhaps you should follow him, the answers are just around the next corner. So you try another doctor in a white coat, or another magic potion with 'drink me' written on it, and neither work but set you back to the start, at the bottom of the tunnel and you wonder what you're doing, as you have been here before, so very many times. And slowly you begin to realise that you have learned more about this place than the people who are drawing the maps and writing the directions, but because you are now a red rose – it is written down and so it must be – no one will believe you. No one can hear you, your mouth is filled with paint. I'm not sure if they can even see you anymore. You have very nearly disappeared completely.

I try to chip off the paint, spit it from my mouth, and go back to tell people what I have seen and what I have learned. If they can only see it isn't red after all, but paint, perhaps I can get them to look for aphids and greenfly, rot or root damage, and perhaps there will be a treatment then.

We must tell what we can, hope others who listen can hear us, and those who look can see us, and gradually, gradually, we may regain our form. In the sharing of these stories perhaps then we will become more than a grin that floats in the trees. All the while, there are packs of cards frantically painting white roses red, just to prove there are no white roses in this garden. There are more than just me. We have all been painted red. Our records show we are red, and so must always have been, and always will be.

I will borrow my stories from others while I construct my own. And as I do this, I will stay and sip soup with the Mock Turtle, and search out Absolem the wise Caterpillar. I will borrow my stories from others: they will make a quilt of patchwork to cover me while I sleep. And I will dream, of tea parties and dances, and of waking to a world where everything is right-side up and front to back.

Occasionally a hedgehog rolls away from the croquet lawn and as it gets up to walk off it looks up, and I see that it sees me, actually sees me. I am still here. And sometimes that is enough. I am not a grin or a rose painted red, but a person with a weird and mysterious illness that no one knows what to do with. And instead of telling me that it's me that's wrong, and I must realise

I am a red rose, the hedgehog reminds me that it's them, they aren't looking, aren't seeing, aren't listening and don't hear me. I remember it's not about changing how I see myself, for I am Alice, and they must change how they look at me.

YOLK

CHIKODILI EMELUMADU

They called me blessed.

I had a thick, proud mane. At four, I noticed the fairy in my hair. Fat and dark and fluffy, she sat camouflaged all through the plaiting in the market, smirked when the woman added beads to the tips to run up the already-doubled bill, darted in and out through the tight plaits causing me to shiver uncontrollably. I asked the aunty doing my hair for a mirror often to peek at what I thought was merely a visitor, and she, taking offence at the imagined childlike criticism of her handiwork, pulled too tightly on my head. At night, the fairy drummed on the taut scalp, plinking strands, making torturous music until I sobbed from the pain, till tiny pus-filled cheers applauded at my temples. She was canny, this fairy, strong. Even after my mother tired of the market women charging extra for the verdant forest on my head and slapped a relaxer on, the fairy hung on like those cats on the posters – *Hang in there, baby.* Lost her smirk a bit, grew anaemic, wispy fingers and toes like the Grinch. Lightened rufescent under sunlight. Hung on by the hair on her chinny-chin-chin.

Twin ogbanje sprites moved into my chest at eight, awake and alert. Bellicose, the pair of them, picking quarrels with doorknobs and elbows. On the playground or in church, it mattered little.

These twins drew attention to themselves, hard and hungry as they were. 'Look at those seeds!' the aunties cried, excited. They touched the knots, twisted them and the sprites snarled and spat. They grew fat and soft on the attention. 'Look at those fruits,' muttered the uncles and the brothers and the fathers, until I cut the sprites off behind a wrought iron balcony, high away from prying eyes and wandering hands. Even so they spat, the sound of water hitting hot fat in a cast iron pan. They raised hard faces, betrayed, and wanting to be set free, but the uncles, you see. One had to be careful. Sprites are beautiful and callous as they are wont, but they are no good in a fight.

The Knife Thrower turned up at eleven, a daemon warrior, slashing, burning. Blood everywhere. Do you want to know? She was a barbarian shapeshifter – at once a short, stout cow with massive horns, and a sea serpent, riding waves of blood, blood, blood, pure muscle and constriction – taking what was given, offering nothing, demanding sacrifice and slaughter, remaining unappeased anyway. She left slashes where I could not see but felt deeply. She left slashes where I could, scarring my hips and buttocks, claiming her territory entirely.

The thing about the fae is that they adapt their behaviour to their surroundings. They eat how we eat, burping if we consider that a compliment, for instance, or blushing at burps if not. In my father's moustache, I saw male fairies hold hands as they talked. I saw elves, children of Ekwensu, the charlatan, as mischievous as they are industrious, steady my mother's knuckles and wrists as she pounded yam, only to urinate over her forehead and into the mortar when she was not looking, resulting in the softest, fluffiest meal we ever tasted. Their bright red bottoms flashed as they worked their magic, helping my mother's healing hands palpate the sick in the hospital and at home, turning out magnificent stews and soups. I watched them grow bored and hobble her feet with little hammers as she slept, causing bunions, because elves must always have work to do or they work you instead.

Igbo fairies are not called fairies at all, but what was it Shakespeare said? 'A rose by any other name would smell as sweet.' It does not matter as much what they are called as how they act. You know them to be fae, we know them as *The Others*. Of 'Humans, The Ndiichie, Wandering Spirits and The Others' fame. Much like us Igbo people, our fae practice the culture of *onye gata o chelu ibe ya*: our fae cannot exist in isolation. They must have a community and so, before you know it, you have hundreds of fairies, congregating in your blood stream, causing mischief in your body, wreaking havoc on your mind, until finally, I, at nineteen and three-quarters, found myself beset by a planet whose orb pushed through the wall of my vagina.

What was I looking for in there? I will tell you. Perhaps you are thinking to yourself 'And why not? Why should she not look there? It is her body.' How mistaken you are and clearly *not* Igbo! Among the first things you learn as an Igbo girl: your body and its inhabitants do not in fact belong to you. Until you marry, when ownership transfers from God/your father/society to your husband. I really had no business looking down there, especially after my A* in Biology at both O Level and GCSE. I could draw the bovine-appearing female reproductive system in my sleep. I could draw a cross-section. I knew about my three holes, instead of two, and what if I had not seen the secret one in nearly two decades of living with it? But oppression breeds rebellion and show me one Igbo woman who is not the strongest, most creative, and most independent-minded person you have ever met? I rest my case.

Wait, I still have not told you what I was looking for down there. Voices. They whispered to me as I slept. Within a few nights they graduated to singing. Such horrible songs, terrible things they said. I clenched my thighs and they laughed and sang louder, such scornful, hurtful songs.

These pests, to all intents and purposes, were private, at least, no adults thought to mention their existence to us and we, in our childhood, learnt to stop talking about them amongst ourselves. Nobody confessed to their own parasites, even when we could clearly see some of them. Nobody informed us that the ugliest creatures grow and are fed on destructive emotions, such as anguish and dread. And guilt. The orb that grew and spread, without pain or discomfort, out of the walls of my vagina contained imps so at odds with the rest of my denizens – scaly and winged at once, taloned, and long of snout – that I began to suspect someone had put them there, infected me with them. I thought I knew who the culprit was, but I cannot name them now even though they are deceased. Family. Society. Shame. Perhaps it was not him anyway, but the other unholy being, whose similarity to Jesus ended in their shared trade. Or, or, or. It matters not.

I tried to hear myself think over the croaking and bellowing, the way the orb swelled and then shrank whenever I tried to have it investigated by medical professionals. My mother first, bending me over the ironing board and reporting 'I did not see anything, she's too hairy,' confirming that suspicion once and for all. Blessed. As above, so below.

The new boyfriend next, my first, and the reason for the guilt on which the imps feasted.

'You're just feeling bad. I have not taken your virginity anyway, I only put the tip.'

Only the tip. Only the tip, but not willingly. Virginity, I have since learned, is sauce for patriarchs, but the coercion ate me up. Or rather, the imps ate *it* up. The resentment. The betrayal. All

I wanted was to be kissed, to be held, gently, tenderly, the sweet swell of orchestral music sounding in my stomach. All I desired was to be cherished for what lay between my ears and not my legs, but men it seems, cannot love without piercing and claiming and wounding completely.

'What are you worried about? I don't see anything,' he said. 'It's in your mind.'

To the gynaecologist then, with the oversized glasses, the twitchy moustache, and I, nervous from being examined by the colleague of my mother's. What did he see? Was I different down there, could he tell I had been touched? Would he tell my parents?

'I don't see anything,' he said, relieved to be done, but I could not take the croaking anymore, and opening up myself, revealed the orb within, now pink, now grey. 'Yes,' he said, wonder infused with curiosity. 'Yes, I see it.'

The surgery would take place at my father's theatre, counting back from one hundred and only getting to ninety-six before I was knocked out. I heard them then, at the precipice of sleep and wakefulness, the ragged 'No' born of realisation.

I woke up in a uterine-pink room. Girls like pink. Alarms bubbled up like bicarbonate of soda through the grog of my sedation. What had I said? Did I reveal too much? Did my parents know what I had been doing?

The orb lay on my bedside cabinet, in a kidney-shaped stainless-steel dish, left there for me by the gynaecologist. He wanted me to see it, his gift. Its malice faded as it died, starved of its favourite foods.

'A congenital cyst,' said my surgeon. 'Never seen anything like it in person. Beautiful. Like an egg without its shell, *abi?*'

Was it malignant? He did not think so, but who knew, who knew how these things turned and when? The body was a funny place.

Lucky me, he caught it in time, pulled it out complete in its sac, but not without a price. An eye for an eye, an orb for sensitivity. My period of John Wayne strutting ended with reduced feeling to the left side of my labia.

They called me blessed. How fortunate that I saw it to begin with. 'But what,' asked my father, a wary gleam in his eye, 'was I looking for there in the first place?'

AND THE
FOREVER HOUSE

LAURA ELLIOTT

There is a woman in my house whose name I do not know. It isn't a big house, my house, but sometimes I think there are rooms in here that even I don't know about. If I think about them for too long it makes me nervous; and it isn't good for me to be nervous. After all, maybe there are other women in these other rooms and maybe some of them have been here for even longer than I have. And wouldn't that be a horror?

I don't like her very much, this new woman in my house, but at least I know she's here. She is sitting in the grey armchair, the one with the flat cushions and the tea stains on the arm. She does that a lot. Sitting, I mean. She sits in the chair, and sometimes she sits on the sofa. At night, she sleeps upstairs in a bed that isn't washed as often as it ought to be. John would have had something to say about that if it were me, but I suppose things are different now.

The woman has long auburn hair and dark eyes, and her skin has the grey tinge of someone who is unwell, even on the rare days she pastes makeup over the top. Blusher helps, but not very much. She is still pale under the paint, and if I didn't watch her so closely and know that she's never fallen or been hit, I would swear that the dark rings under her eyes were real and livid bruises. It's possible, I suppose, to bruise from the inside-out, but on the days when the sunlight streams through the windows and the golden hour falls across her face, she looks like something already dead.

She didn't used to sit here every day. There was a time when she only came back to sleep, and I liked her better then. It's difficult to share a house with someone you don't know, and at least when she was gone I could enjoy my own space. The living room walls were red, back then, and the kitchen freshly painted. The woodchip in the hall was perfect for digging my fingernails into, and I'd made good progress on the bedroom's awful wallpaper.

Now, one living room wall is a deep royal blue, and the others are an anaemic white. I'm sure from the outside it's more calming than before, but blue is a dreadfully difficult colour to see out of, you know. I've taken to slipping into the white walls instead, but their curious blankness offends me, and I start to feel exposed.

Some days, I imagine the woman in the armchair can see me, creeping about inside the white, and I wonder what I must look like to her. Perhaps, when the sun shines just so, I cast some sort of a shadow. I ought to be more careful when the golden hour comes, and the whole room glows a sudden yellow, because surely, that is when my silhouette crosses the grey of her face? She screws up her eyes and pulls the tatty old blanket over her head. A few days ago she even called for the man to come and close the curtains to block out the last of the light.

I like the man better than the woman, probably because he comes and goes. He's here more often recently, but he's always got something to do. He cooks, and he cleans, and he pulls shut the curtains when she asks. He taps away at his computer and he takes care of the cat. He reminds me of John, in a way, except he doesn't tell her what to do. Oh, how useful that would have been to me, when we first took up in our house!

*

I am starting to resent the other woman. I can't think with all her stillness, and the little pained groans she makes. This house has seen parties, and heartbreaks, and new tenants moving in and out. Now, it's so quiet and so still, I think I could go quite mad.

I think the woman knows this, too, so it's at least one thing we share. During the day, while the man works upstairs, she gets up to stretch her legs. And sometimes, on good days, she bends at the waist and tries to put her hands on the floor. Whenever she succeeds, I think: *A-ha! Soon you will be gone, and I will be left alone in peace!*

But oh, how she shakes with the slightest exertion. How her muscles tremble and her teeth chatter and her jaw gets so tight with pain that even I can feel the headache behind her eyes.

'You're definitely sick,' I tried to tell her once, but she, of course, didn't hear me.

I was sick too, once upon a time, but I'm glad mine wasn't such a serious case. A whole year it's been. and she doesn't seem to be getting better. A year is a long time to be trapped between these walls, and even though she visits the doctor, they don't seem to care. How could they, when they leave her alone in here?

*

She visited a doctor today, and then cut off all her hair. Great long strands of glorious red tumbled into the bathroom sink. I watched from behind the tiles, even though they leeched the heat from my heart, while she hacked away at her flowing locks and cropped them close to her scalp.

'Stress,' she kept saying, in a tone of disbelief. 'Is that the best they can do?'

And as her hair fell away, she cried and she cried, to see the matted mess in the sink.

I confess, I felt a twinge of sympathy for her. She only has energy to shower once a week, and while her hair hung in knotted clumps against her neck, it really was beautiful once.

*

For the last few weeks I've been keeping away from the white walls, when the light catches them just so, but I'm more convinced than ever that the other woman knows I'm here. When she returned from the doctor's this morning her face was hard with anger, but she waited for the man to go upstairs before she started to speak.

'This is my life,' she whispered quite softly, until I had to creep closer to hear. And then, again, with dawning horror:

'Doesn't anybody care?'

*

I think I might have judged her too harshly, the other woman in her chair. As the years drag on I'm starting to see that she's the most interesting thing in here. My daily routine is now built around hers, and it goes a little something like this:

At 9:30am, the man gets her up and helps her to sit up in bed. He brings her a coffee and she takes a pill, and I watch her struggle to wake. She blinks and winces in the morning sun and all of her joints crack. Her muscles shake and her jaw draws tight, and her skin flushes red with the strain.

By 11:00am she often makes it downstairs, and for an hour or so seems okay, but I'm no stranger to faking health, and I know her tells too well. She makes the man tea, and fixes her breakfast, and curls herself up in her chair. When he goes upstairs to continue his day, that's when her skin fades to grey.

*

I'm not scared of her seeing me anymore. In fact, I hope that she does. I've started to creep through the white and shake the wall by her head. I think she's starting to notice, and more than once she's lurched from her chair. Yesterday, she pressed her hand to the paint, to help her to stand up straight. Her eyes were unfocused and they bounced up and down, as though she was watching the room shudder.

'I'm here!' I called, as she clutched her head. 'I know you can see me too.'

But she vomited up the breakfast she'd made, and the man came running down the stairs.

I hid in the blue wall before he arrived. I wonder if he could see me. I ought to be careful, I'm starting to think, in case he catches me creeping.

I can't forget - although I've tried - how John so hated to see me creep.

*

He left today to go to work, which means I have her all to myself. There's something quite different when the man goes away and she doesn't have to pretend to be well. She talks out-loud, for one thing, and I imagine she's talking to me.

'Why won't they believe me?' She asked today.

'Because you're a woman,' I told her.

And then she stood and stared at the wall, and I shook and I shook and I shook.

*

I've been thinking about the rooms of this house. How many there are just like this. How many women in how many rooms in how many houses are locked away with no one to listen? At least the other woman has me here, even though she doesn't know. The man will come back in a couple of days, but she will have heard me by then.

I've been creeping about, you see, even though I know that I shouldn't. I've found rooms upon rooms upon rooms just like this, each with their own sad prisoners. There's Bertha in the attic, and Dora in the snug, and Charlotte tucked up in bed, and so many others, nameless and forgotten, who I'm certain I can wake, bit-by-bit.

I'm not sure what kind of home we've made, that can keep on growing like this. I imagine it stretches across the whole world and towers up into the sky. It burrows beneath the ragged Earth and coils like a serpent through the rock. But it must be invisible, this warren of rooms, or else how could anyone bear it? Perhaps it's too silent, or perhaps we're made small, when no-one bothers to hear us.

*

There's not much time before I lose her forever. Some doors will never open again. The golden hour's here and I know that she can see me. She clambers up from her chair. I have an army behind me, shaking the walls, and she has no choice but to listen. I wonder how long it will take her now, to chip the paint from the brick? To pull off the paper and burn the house down, and free us. One voice at a time.

THE SISTERHOOD OF BROKEN DOLLS

BEVERLEY BUTCHER

I am sitting outside the operating theatre in a hospital gown, wearing mustard yellow espadrilles with bottle-green compression socks.

'Sexy, huh?' I say to the anaesthetists' assistant as she completes the consent form. A stray tear slides down my face, but I think I catch it before she sees.

'Do you understand the procedure you are having today?' she asks.

I nod.

'Wide local excision of the right breast. Removal of invasive lobular carcinoma, plus sentinel node biopsy,' I say.

She raises an eyebrow over her surgical mask. 'Are you a nurse?'

'Yes,' I say, and another tear bleeds down my face.

It crept along the ducts and lobules, feathering out like a secret army. I had no idea it was there. No lump, no indentations, no sedition of the flesh. A letter in the post from the local medical university requested my assistance in a study: rates of breast cancer detection in women over fifty. Would I mind? Just a questionnaire. Fill in your history, the longevity of women in your family.

Family history of breast cancer? Nil.

Age of your maternal grandmother at death? 93.

Age of paternal grandmother at death? 93.

Age of own mother, if still alive? 93.

I continue filling in details of aunts who lived past ninety; a pride of corn-fed women approaching a Royal telegram centenary, and two surpassing it. Women brought up in remote villages, breathing fresh air, living on the food they'd grown in little market gardens during the war years. My maternal grandmother, taking in local children whose parents were sick, war evacuees, and once, an infant left on her doorstep with a note that read:

'Please take my baby. He'll have a better life with you'.

These unstoppable Goddesses.

One last thing, the study requests: please attend for a mammogram. Here is your appointment.

I arrive at the mobile unit outside the local cottage hospital. Inside, an intricate spider-dance begins. I am choreographed by a cheerful radiographer in an appropriation of the Time Warp dance from Rocky Horror– 'Step back! To the side! Stick out your bum! Look up!' while my breasts are sandwiched in Perspex and photographed from different angles. I am pleased to tuck them back into my clothes, pink and stinging, and get on with my working day. 'That's it for another three years', I think, and triumphantly drive to another hospital to begin work.

One appointment leads to another. They thread like glass beads on a sinister necklace, the shape of which cannot yet be fully determined. I secretly hope this chain of unfolding events does not turn into a biting serpent, but it is a distant thought, a far-off tide, and besides, I have the good genes of the Goddesses in my favour. I attend for a biopsy - tissue grabbed from within the breast and pulled out, like a tiny worm, to be sent to histology.

'It would be prudent to look at what exactly this area is,' says the doctor, pointing to a white knot on the screen.

'It'll be nothing!' I say. 'No history of anything in my family.'

But family history can be re-written. I could be the first. The outlier, the pioneer.

But what about the yoga, the careful hydration, the generations of Goddesses? I enter a conference call with myself, an inner debate of frantic searching.

'What about your hand in the staff room tuck box, the long hours ignoring your physical needs, the thirteen-hour shifts?'

'The recreational drugs in the 90s, all those weekends drinking, dancing? What about the little matter of those, Nursey, eh? You wouldn't catch the Goddesses drinking gin cocktails, or eating disco biscuits, or walking home shoeless in a sequinned dress, or...'

'But that was so long ago! I was allowed to enjoy myself, wasn't I?'

You brought this on yourself. Yourself.

You and your body are not one, you are now divided. Just like the cell division inside your breast, spilling over, popping like popcorn.

I pass from the sisterhood of nursing into the sisterhood of broken dolls, and I have but one question;

'Can you get it out of me? Can you make it stop?'

The doctor draws something on a thin piece of paper.

'This will explain it a bit,' she says, and pushes it to me. My eyes are glassed and staring. I do not absorb the lines and curves on the sheet and fold it carefully until it is small, then put it in my pocket.

*

Cancer is an abduction. It uses several forms of transport to perform its dirty work.

I was skipping along and stopped to look at a pretty flower, then *BANG*! It jumped out of the bushes, put a bag over my head and pulled me into a waiting car.

I can't see anything. Can't see the road ahead.

I'm not reading a news item aloud, I'm not remarking on the awfulness of someone else's predicament, this is me. It's me.

As you would say to any kidnapper:

Where are we going?

What's happening?

Please. Don't kill me.

After the abduction and the car, in this journey you did not agree to, you find yourself in an empty train carriage, an old fashioned, spooky one with dusty cushioned seats and wooden windows. It is night-time. The train clatters over the points mournfully, and you doubt there is a driver.

It pushes on, not offering to slow down. There is a vague light outside. There must be something up ahead. You have climbed onto the seat and pulled open the window, straining to see. Your face is pressed into the night air, the rush, the engine noise, the faint hope that it will be something good.

An illuminated station draws closer, with figures on the platform. You recognise them, they're waiting for you. Your husband, your children. You push one arm out the window, contorting your body, stretching your fingers, calling their names. The train won't slow. Their haunted faces flash by. The youngest boy chases the train down to the platform's end, and you think you hear him shout 'Mum!' but this driverless train doesn't care and will not stop.

Other stations flash by, with more people on the platform: your friends, who call your name and cheer words of encouragement and throw flowers onto the tracks as if to decrease the journey's terror. All the faces read: *come back, come back, come back*, but the train rhythm cries *we're going, we're going, we're going.*

Then your elderly parents, silent, strained, bewildered, who trust you to get things done because you're a nurse. You're sensible. You're a descendent of the unstoppable Goddesses.

All they can do is watch the train carry you away.

Their faces say: *it was supposed to be us first. Not you.*

The clattering points turn into the awful tick-tick-tick of pulleys. You are now on a roller coaster carriage climbing upwards. The track is unlit. You assume a fairground and the seaside from gentle, rhythmic rasp water distantly, but otherwise, all is black. You suspect the nothingness is inhabited by shadows and serpents. Why wouldn't it be? You think about being sixteen when roller coasters were a thrill, in yellow summer sunshine, or lit up in multicoloured illumination. There is a pause at the top in which you inhale all your powerlessness and mortality. There might be one lone star above, for company, but it cannot detract from what you now know: the only way is down, but how far, and how fast, cannot be foretold.

And then it all comes at once.

The moment of suspension is over, and the hurtling plunge loses you. The poetry of starlight is sucked out of the universe.

You hear screams.

There must be others.

You cannot turn.

There is no room right now.

This your track, your journey, your singular terror, and you must face forward and keep going.

*

I lie in weeds outside my childhood home, having been spat out of the rollercoaster. The house has broken windows and a boarded door. A sign says 'Danger – Do Not Enter'.

Grey clouds boil in a pre-storm sky, and witches on broomsticks circle the chimney pots, cackling. All is not done yet.

The door is mobbed with ivy. I pull it away and try the handle. I enter freely, just as I would have done when arriving home from school, then college, to a familiar rush of cooking, and warm ironing, and homeliness. The house is precisely as it was in 1985. I expect to find my mother complaining about Dad laying down a greasy spanner on the kitchen worktops, or my brother lying sprawled out on the telephone, sucking a round lollipop. Instead, it feels like they're on holiday and have left me behind to house-sit.

There are no signs of dilapidation inside, just an engulfing overload of familiarity; the creak on the third stair, the unseen dog shaking his collar and rattling his name-tag, the blossomy smell of carpet freshener. I climb the stairs to my bedroom. Fragments of popular tunes from 1985 play in my head. The old man in the next house along can be seen cutting roses. A crop sprayer flies lazily over.

I sit on my bed.

The wooden chest in the alcove, where I kept childhood toys, secret teenager things, is still there. The key is in the place it always is. The instincts and habits remain fresh, after all these years. I unlock the chest and look at the contents. Inside the lid is a mirror. I jolt to see myself not as a teenager, but as I am now. Older. Softer. Less intense. More 'Mum'.

I find my old doll in the toybox, with dark lashed blue eyes. When she is tilted backwards, her eyes close; sit her up, and they open. She is naked and has an arm missing.

She regards me with one eye open and one closed, her functionality reduced after years of love from a little girl who wanted to mend the doll's broken arm after her brother pulled it from its plastic moulded socket.

I see my image in the mirror, clothed in the hospital gown, a splash of iodine solution across the right breast of the thin fabric. When I look down at myself, I am as naked as the doll. I draw her close to my body, a gentle Madonna. I notice I have been operated on.

One breast has its nipple intact; an open, innocent eye looking out at the changed landscape of the body, looking for danger. The other breast is eyeless, or closed, a narrative scar across its centre where the tumour and the nipple have been removed. I examine it, run my finger along its ridges. I am struck by the thought that on a good day, it could be winking, cheekily, announcing to the world 'I'm still here, sugar cups!'

On a bad day, it could be sleeping in practice for death. The closure of the wound. The closing of the eye, never more to open. My body is already exploring its changed personality.

I consider my sixteen-year-old self again; no reason to value my body as precious, no reason to stop, to think about it. A body for simple and multiple pleasures: a vehicle and a vessel, to get places and enjoy myself once there. To move quickly and sinuously, never stopping by the side of the open road, never pausing in snaking pursuit of enjoyment. A sidewinder over desert sands. A racehorse over plains. Admire my shanks. Press yourself into me, lose yourself. I will lose myself too, in night-stock scented evenings of warm breath and skin, across the fields, in the woods, in the village churchyard.

I fired like a gun across the landscape. I was tall and slim, a physical presence curated by living outdoors and those Goddess genes. I was compared to my paternal grandmother, described universally as 'an elegant woman in her time'.

I only knew her as a cardiganed widow, looking out of her draughty farmhouse into the next world. I slid my high arched feet into high heels and walked tall as a field-flower into city life.

Is that what did it?

Is it a punishment for leaving the countryside?

Or did it start when I lived in the country?

Perhaps it was that time when I had a little herb garden, and I went out in the Chernobyl rain, the same rain that killed my bay tree. Just tell me, so I can make it all better. So I can get back on friendly terms with my body. That long-legged, slender limbed, gently curving, flexible body. That trailing honeysuckle.

Betrayed me.

Stealth-bombed me.

Fucked me over.

But I can't run over the fields, away from my body, despite its betrayal. I cannot abandon it.

I have to stay and take my turn to be nursed.

*

I enter a hushed clinic. There are rows of seated angels, with shorn hair and luminous eyes, and in my terror, I believe it to be a waiting room for death. But I am mistaken; despite their serenity, this is no celestial threshold. This is the place where we come to get fixed. The doll's hospital.

With silent confirmation, we have a shared knowledge: that all of us have arrived here after the same abduction, and train, and rollercoaster, and childhood visitations.

Through a window are the unbroken dolls, who urge us to fight, and run races for us, and bring soothing and pretty gifts; but we are in mists and cannot see the ground beneath us; not yet.

The air burdens with colours of black and red, the shades of chemical devilment. The dolls remain placid as slow water, sucking the necessary evil through their veins. Flowers, lilies, leaf capillaries, filling with a decoction that balances life and death.

Someone calls my name, and I am asked to lie on my back in a room filled with humming machinery and laser beams. A large metal eye circles me, a camera obscura taking in the precise measurements of who I am, what I am, and why I am here. I lay back and look up at the sunlit picture of treetops on the ceiling. The mousetrap litany begins.

What did you do to bring this on?

How did you make this happen?

Think, Nurse, think!

I stare hard into the ceiling picture of maple branches and leaves. Through the scorched oranges and seared reds, patches of blue are opening up.

It occurs to me that the answers cannot tumble, perfectly formed, from the sky. There is the possibility that nothing caused it. It just happened. That for a split second, for reasons unknown, I resonated with the rebellion of cancer, and within my body, the mutiny took hold.

My cancer is not a foe, it is a teacher. It erects a sign on a dangerous country road that says: 'Priorities Changed Ahead'.

Distantly, a bell rings, and there are cheers. Someone is home safe, and my eyes fill with tears of gratitude. The bell for the end of treatment. A doll who can go home, if not intact, alive. The kidnappers did not claim her. In the room of humming equipment, the scene repeats for days until I feel nauseous and tired.

I close my eyes in acceptance. When I open them, I am in my own garden, shaded on a mellow summer afternoon. The only humming is that of bees in industry. I unfold the piece of paper the doctor drew for me, and study the depiction, in pencil, of the anatomy of a breast. The lobules are arranged like petals. Within them, the smaller ducts are arranged like rosebuds. The breast is represented as a flower, or a mandala, going on to infinity.

I put a hand to the indented breast and feel the subtraction of flesh that has saved my life. My healed scar is a timeline back to the beginning of the journey. A rail track of the nightmare ride, now sunlit and seeded with wildflowers.

We join hands, the broken dolls, the Goddesses and I, and take a walk there, together, in the sun.

THE ANIMAL
AT MY CHEST

JANE HARTSHORN

I am getting my photo taken. It's Christmas and I sit surrounded by wrapping paper and curls of metallic ribbon. *Shut your legs*, my mother says. Ruffle of a satin dress. White oblong of a gusset. I am suddenly self-conscious. *I always sit like this*, I say.

The sisters next door push their toy prams up and down, up and down, and I join them with a stuffed dog on a lead. My mother buys me a Tiny Tears doll, which includes a potty and pull-up knickers. A party dress with frilled sleeves. Barefoot along the lane behind our house, I drag the doll on a belt taken from my mother's wardrobe, a band of leather around her neck. The dress gathers straggles of bedstraw. The small hooked hairs of burr seeds latching onto the lace as though crawling into animal fur.

The sponge of moss between my toes feels good. The slugs stick to my arms and legs, a fretwork of greenish secretions across my skin. *Don't let her play with them.* I am told not to touch the yellow flowers on the next-door neighbour's tree. Petals like a praying mantis. The tree drapes itself languidly across the adjoining wall, its silver seed pods dangling like crescent moons. I make a potion of crushed flowers and grass. Add a handful of yellow petals. It congeals into a muddy paste, souring on my tongue. Coating my teeth, slippery like milk skin.

I am twelve when I catch my first rabbit. Its eyes glued shut like candied cherries. I hold it to my breast and feel its heart thumping against mine. When I let it go, it struggles under a fence and catches its gummed-up eye on the wire. A teacher phones the house concerned. *She's good with animals*, my mother tells her.

On holiday, a blur of chestnut, cloven-toed and crashing above our heads like a felled tree. The windshield smeared with blood and fur. We sit in the dark of the car, breathing heavily. As we drive off, I look behind me. See the deer hobbling into the trees, its neck limp. My father's hands trembling on the steering-wheel.

It appears under my arms first. Wet, newborn, fawn down. I am pleased. It keeps coming. Darker whorls. Knots on pinewood. The girl asks if she can look. Pushes her breasts against the glass of the shower door. Steam and pink flesh. I know to hide it. I have an idea that something is going wrong. I imagine growing a thick pelt of dark hair. That way no one will know.

The girls start shaving their legs. Hairless baby rabbits. Pink razors from Boots lit up like Barbie dolls in plastic packaging. I pluck mine at night. My mother calls them the wiry ones; small skelfs of hair greying under the skin. Wing-cased beetles growing horizontal. Afterwards, the shards dark on my palm. Brittle little exoskeletons.

My father takes me to his friend's house. The friend serves me a plate of sausages. The skin white and sticky, bulging in the places where the meat pulses. I refuse to eat and my father smacks me for embarrassing him. His handprint raised mauve on my thigh. When he comes to kiss me goodnight, I smell salted peanuts on his breath.

Running down a hill in a field, I slip, and something cracks open. Lies misshapen on the grass. I try to explain how it feels. *Like a telephone*, I say. I have to pick it up and put it down. *Put it on the table*, the doctor says to my father. It is taking longer to heal than is normal. The bone knits itself together, the narrow fissure stitching shut. My arm stiffens into an angular shape, and I hold it slightly away from me, as though it is just an object I'm carrying.

We go to Holy Isle, father and daughter. There is a basin carved into the hill, an altar with offerings of dead hyacinth heads, turrets of small stones, slip of lichen dampening its sides. Sweet smell of something going bad. A caterpillar floats on the surface, belly up, tumescent white. Skin slackened, a few bristles left near the wrinkled base. I do not tell my father what I have seen.

Men keep looking at me like they know. They can smell the cloying odour of damp earth. Hair matted with blood. The spots of heat blistering the breastbone, the small of the back. The spread of freckles seeded strawberry across my shoulders. At school, we sit in a row along a gym bench and pick the hairs from one another's blazers. The strands web dark between her fingers like brown mulch at the bottom of a pond.

A man I recognise appears by the side of the road. He holds out his hand and asks me to take it. I am afraid he will pull me down the grassy verge to the trees beyond. Under my crisp white shirt, the curve of my breast. The tiny sprig of creases where the button stretches the cotton. I keep walking. My school shirt greasy and fetid below the armpits. Tangle of something greying by the dirty water, caught in the branches. An old t-shirt, or underwear. Its neck wrung out like a bird's.

Catching the feathered seed-heads of grass, rubbing the grains between my fingers. White spittle where the stalk forks. An angle like the corner of a mouth. My finger probing, will no longer listen. My hands have a secret language. They remember objects long after I have. Handle of a mug. A shopping bag. In silence, I read the shapes for clues. I want to know where they have been. The hands grapple furtively under my sheets. Practicing their new lexicon. My brain unclenching.

I start to take time off school, the gown with blue diamonds pinching the hair at the nape of my neck. A long triangle of pink visible as I bend from the waist. The red welt where my bra has lacerated the flesh. My weight is a test I keep failing. He always seems so sad, as though I have done it on purpose. He tells my mother I should eat more red meat and fatty foods. After dinner, I hide mouthfuls of beef stew in the soil of the monstera, pushing strings of half-chewed gristle towards the gleam of roots.

The words I have forgotten, I keep in a pale green soapbox. Testing myself on the edges of sleep, I chant *hoover, toaster, hose*. I practice in the bathroom mirror. Try to detect signs of change around my mouth. *Carp carp carp*, as I remove my makeup. *Cranium cranium cranium*, as I brush my teeth. Their shapes are unfamiliar in my throat, snarling my vocal cords like the serrated teeth of a conifer cone.

Between tests, I rest. Wake in the middle of the afternoon, sweat-sheened and dreaming I am inside the machine. Its rivulets of sound throbbing damp between my legs. My hair curdling at the base of my neck, a fibrous mass. A tangle of broken follicles clotting dark across the pillow.

The hairs have become harder to remove. I spot them around my nipple. Between my knuckles. The bud just visible below the skin. Unwinding long and dark like insect legs when I tweezer them. I cut the blistered yellow on the sole of my foot with nail scissors. Sometimes I cut too deep, and bleed a bouquet of red across my bed sheets.

I gnaw at the wood of my bedpost. Pine dust coating my lips. I start to bury things inside myself, like what it feels like to roll down my tights. The cold of the gel against my skin. A girl in school demands I hold out my arm. *See I'm not as skinny as her*, she says. It's impossible to wriggle free.

At night, the squirm in my abdomen wakes me and I drag myself to the bathroom, my leg catching on the corner of the door frame. My foot pale and blotchy like a dead bird, waterlogged and flapping at an odd angle on the tiles. My skin stretch-marked purple from the animal at my chest.

When I can no longer walk, a nurse comes to the house and gives me an injection for the swelling. She wears purple latex gloves and stays for half an hour in case I have a reaction. One day, she teaches me how to inject myself and I never see her again. I always choose the same spot, slightly to the left of the largest freckle on my thigh. I spend my days soaking in Epsom salts, waiting for the skin to loosen around my bones. Long, papery strips like sycamore bark ribbon the circumference of the bath, glistening against the mint enamel.

That winter, the frost comes early. Goldfish rise to the top of the pond encased in ice. I chip one out with nail scissors. Keep it in a soap dish in my underwear drawer. Each morning, I examine it for changes. The fins and tail dry out first, pressed flat like nasturtium petals. Its scales distended, bleached white and flaking, revealing tiny diamonds of coral flesh.

By spring, I am able to leave the house again. The soil soothes my elbows and knees, scraped raw from carpet burn. Moist like a poultice. My father walks a few paces behind me, and I can hear the jangle of the leash in his hand. I find a nest unattended and stick my head between twigs and leaves. I carefully lift out the first nestling. Its mouth opens like a yellow crocus, the pearl of its unopened eye rolling beneath the lid. He makes a sound, indistinct like a voice muffled in the dark. I am feeling less like myself every day.

ASLYM

IRENOSEN OKOJIE

I am walking our dog in the park when the burning sensation infiltrates my throat as though it is new found land. The burning sensation makes me want to slip into the abandoned baby harness slung over a bench then run towards a baying that escapes the heat in my blood. The burning sensation has instructions for daylight. *In you. Out of you. Beyond you.* The burning sensation says the fog expanding in your brain has accomplices. The burning sensation warns the alphabet in your mouth will collide with lightening. I have the urge to place my dog on the swing, the creak of it is music, a calming balm, or in the silver slide winding into a sandpit studded with bright plastic buckets and shovels, I think of placing her on the multicoloured roundabout decorated with treats that glimmer then vanish. She, a barking compass as the roundabout turns, as the world spins. I am myself yet I do not feel quite right. There is a thundering in my ears. My skin is clammy and warm. A heat rises in me. My mouth is dry with panic. There are clusters of people in the wide open park spaces, small colonies waiting to be ruptured by something dark, voracious and relentless. My dog tugs on the leash wanting to rummage for bones, oiled chip wrappers, coins with disintegrating bodies wielding knowing gazes.

Two nights later, it is just before midnight. I am standing in my room by the wardrobe when the taste leaves my tongue. It is sudden, intense, acute. My mother lingers in the doorway in her signature style, partially in and out of a room, talking about so and so relative who did not show up to a cousin's baby's naming ceremony back home. Her voice fades. The burning sensation in my throat escalates. Pathways there close up. There is a lump in my throat. I sense an alien force hijacking my system. I feel it moving inside me. My body is no longer mine alone. It is a host for something malevolent. I cannot breathe. I am feverish. My heart rate increases to a frenetic pace. My mouth seems constricted. I cannot open it to its full circumference.

We call the ambulance service. The operator asks me a hundred questions. A medical professional will ring me back he says, but he is not sure when. Besides, he does not think this is urgent. I put the phone down in frustration. I am a Black woman. I do not have the time to fully rely on systems where the odds are stacked against me. I trust my instincts instead. We call a cab to the hospital. At the A&E department, after checking my stats, the doctor confirms my worst fears. It is the virus for sure. He states: you have a 50/50 chance because of your breathing issues. It will get worse before it gets better and I don't want to lie to you, it may not get better. I leave that room in a trance. It feels impossible to swallow properly. I am more aware of the sensation than ever. My every movement through the waiting area is heightened. I cannot see what the facial expressions are of those around me. They are a blur. Only the cracked blue siren spinning ahead holds my attention, ready to shatter once I pass through the exit doors.

I watch the news. A man in Kolkata dies from the virus, they say. He leaves behind a sweet shop and a wife. Three days later, his wife dies of a heart attack. I wonder what they dream of now in the afterlife. A childless couple, I wonder who will inherit their dreams that remain on earth.

At night, I see parts of my body abscond onto the fading white lines in the park that form parameters for shadows to dodge. My throat is studded with constellations, curved and hovering above the line like a weapon ready for activation. My concave chest spilling antibiotic pills that will do nothing to curb the enemy, my lungs leaking childhood memories into the goalpost, which resurface partially, in ways that are out of sync. My body is drunk with sickness, mutating under a harsh, foreign glare of light that is not recognisable. Not of the sky or electric bulbs, not of the lamps that I bend my head to in the dark like moored conspirators, writing poems at night urgently. The glare is misshapen, orange hued. A fever decorated with blood spots.

I go for slow walks. I struggle to breathe if I move too quickly. My chest hurts. I hear the sound of a thousand headless kingfishers fluttering towards me, released from the faded hands of ancestors, slipping their bright feather under my tongue as nature's thermometer, pressing their jittery bodies into mine as though leaning into an unruly species. Shrinking back again from me, imposter suns on the move into another horizon. The fever glare takes breaks from me, too, when I am outside. I see it shrouding the hands of a woman sitting at a bus stop, turning a wind-up soldier in her hand. It surrounds the head of a boy flicking through a copy of the Evening Standard magazine outside the DLR station. It seeps into a dead fox on the road, its final pained expression oddly recognisable. Its innards splayed out on the concrete gruesomely.

A man in America needs multiple pints of blood. The virus is eating through his blood and body voraciously, at an Olympian rate. The doctors do not know what to make of it. He is surrounded by strangers, machines but no family. It is the cruellest alienation in a time of need. I hope that he is dreaming in the lonely hours.

At the hospital, after doing a chest x-ray, I pass a ward with carcasses that share one pulse sitting up in beds wearing stethoscopes, holding weathered exit signs. I am lost, crossing one too many doors. Taking several left turns that all lead to points of sickness. Finally, back to the room in Majors, I climb onto the bed awkwardly, careful not to split the paper towel-like sheeting over it which tears somewhat anyway. I stare at the hulking cream machine to my right that checks a multitude of things in the body. The screen is lit but Super Mario is running across it. He will fragment into my heart rate per minute.

An older, portly Black male nurse comes in to take my bloods. He is gregarious and cannot stop talking. He calls me sister. He searches for a vein. He speaks to me with the kind of freedom and intimacy that occurs when Black people are solely in a space free of inhibitions. *Kai! We are dying in droves from this virus, he says. It is everywhere. Plenty frontline staff gone my sister. Several I know. One ambulance driver used to bring me pepperoni pizza sometimes, bring me lamb biryani. Neville, a giant of a man with a big heart. He had time for everybody. Gone just last week. I start my shift beginning of this week and the other nurses tell me he didn't make it. He leaves behind two daughters, a wife. Can you imagine?*

My mouth is frozen. A slither of doom crawls up my spine. I am certain the machine is beeping loudly but the nurse is oblivious. Super Mario is attempting to escape it. He does not know how he got there in the first place. The nurse keeps talking. My throat constricts. My expression is twisted. I am sure I will fall off that bed. I am convinced I will scramble away. I will use the whiteboard listing patients in the nurses' area as a hover board. I will perform a disappearing act worthy of Houdini if it means I can get away from more bad news. Then he finishes, placing a cotton ball and plaster over the needle point in my skin as bulbs of blood seep through it. He breezes out in the same cheery fashion he came in, off to deliver more tales to unsuspecting patients, clutching my blood samples like liquid jewels. I cannot breathe. The doctor tells me they are inundated. I am struggling to breathe for up to eight hours a day, I say. There is nothing they can do for me. They are only admitting those who need to be on ventilators. I oscillate between panic and short-lived relief. I am scared to be in the hospital. I am scared not to be there.

A school teacher in Arizona dies from the virus. Initially told she had a sinus infection, they say. Her students loved her, they say. The image of her smiling warmly holds endless moments that can never be fully translated to an outsider's eye. I wonder where her dreams will go. I ponder over who will collect them on the other side.

I see my lungs in the garden, edging towards the wonky washing line as though it has wisdom to impart.

I am locked away in my room for a month where time slows down. I do not sleep at night in case I do not wake up. I drink Supermalt. I research people who survived the virus. I take notes.

I sleep in the daytime. I do deep breathing exercises at least four times a day. My grandmother rings me every Sunday from Benin, praying for me, speaking in tongues whilst slowly going blind. She commandeers the spirits to guide me. My father, on a solar power research trip in the wilds of Benin, recommends boiling and drinking African herbs one cannot find in Britain. My older brother in Montreal asks what's taking me so long to beat it? As if I hold the solution to a global pandemic with no cure on the horizon. I do not see my younger brother for two months. He is away but we have wonderful video chats. Every day, he video calls me without fail. It is an anchor, his sheer determination to ensure I do not fall into a slipstream of darkness to carry me away. We get to know each other in ways that feel new, invigorating.

I cannot embrace my family. My sister refuses to stop herself from bursting into my room on the odd occasion, her already worried expression crumpling even more. I am unable to hug our dog, who understands that something is amiss. She scratches at my room door. She follows me when I make appearances in the kitchen, whimpering, wagging her tail, performing her favourite trick of standing on her hind legs and opening the fridge door to amuse me. There are more terrible breathing episodes and emergencies. More trips to the hospital. In cab rides on the way there, my mother takes to looking at photos of my younger self, crying silently. I do not dare to interpret what this means in her mind. I tell her to put the photos away.

I am still here.

I must write letters to everyone I care about. I have to share our best memories in them. I must inform them of the joys they have brought to my life. I write a short story, a retelling of an old folk tale made pertinent by my hand. I am determined to fight. I am more stubborn than ever. Even in sickness.

I buy a mesh inhaler, an asthma pump, an oximeter, a thermometer. Instruments to monitor fluctuations in my body, to curb the panic when it comes. I check my body every day. I reach for these items when the airways in my throat start closing up, when my hands flutter there like the heads of ill-fated flamingos, when my chest feels as though it will cave in. During periods of insomnia, I imagine the items leaving our house, returning in the morning to the gap beneath my door covered with permutations of possible cures. I am tired frequently. I try to push through. I avoid communal spaces. I must not infect anyone. I do not want to be seen struggling for breaths. The fear in their eyes is too palpable, the helplessness, the sense that fate will decide.

A 75-year-old man dies in Eastbourne from the virus due to underlying health conditions. A 34-year-old man from Los Angeles dies too after visiting Disney World. I am heart broken by the amount of loss. It is staggering. I wonder if their dreams will reconfigure in the ether.

I wait. Whilst waiting, I hold onto possibilities as sustenance.

I think of all the things I have not done.

I have never scaled the Inca trail in Machu Picchu.
I have never been reborn in the waters of Socotra.
I have never whispered a wish into the ears of statues in Ghana.
I have never searched for migrated birthmarks in the palm lines of women in Madagascar.
I have never fallen in love with an astronaut.

Three months pass.

One blustery morning, I step outside. I am at the front gate but really on the brink still. Fate is the Frankenstein-like creature stumbling in the traffic infected, holding a bottle of Supermalt with my vein throbbing inside it. There are syringe needles pinned around his mouth. There is a tiny, darting golden green chameleon shooting from this saliva coated enclave. *Come on*, he urges tersely, his leaking grey eyes bulging out. He waves me over, the skin peeling from his left hand; he is clutching the lump in my throat in his right hand like new fruit, mirroring it back to me. The pressure in my chest returns. There is an internal rhythm going haywire. My mouth is the shrunken Kalahari desert. An intense splintering of sound in my brain occurs as though it will split then form its own hallucinations. My skin is slick with sweat. I take a deep breath. I am in pain but I do not hesitate. I walk towards fate, asking him about my share of fresh dew from the bottle; informing him of the versions of myself I will breathe life into, ready for me, ready for anything in the waiting, hollowed unrecognisable world.

BIOGRAPHIES

ABI HYNES is a drama and fiction writer based in Manchester. Her plays have been staged in venues across the UK, and she is currently working on original audio drama and TV projects. Her short stories have been widely published, most recently in *Black Static*, *Lucent Dreaming* and *Neon Magazine*, and she was shortlisted for the Bath Flash Fiction Novella-in-Flash Award in 2018. She won the Cambridge Short Story Prize in 2020.

LAUREN BROWN, born in Australia and now living in London, is an emerging writer and editor in legal publishing. Formerly a performance and installation artist, she is now working on her debut novel about reconciling with our past and facing the distortions in our family narratives.

BEVERLEY BUTCHER has published several short stories that range in theme from nursing to rural eerie. Her poem 'Before You Came' is popular worldwide and used in naming ceremonies. She was diagnosed with breast cancer in 2020. She lives in Manchester and works as a Mental Health Practitioner.

LAURA ELLIOTT is a twenty-something disabled writer and journalist. Her short fiction has been published by *Strix Magazine*, STORGY, and others, and she has an essay forthcoming in Monstrous Regiment's *So Hormonal* anthology. You can find her screaming into the void on Twitter at @TinyWriterLaura.

CHIKODILI EMELUMADU was born in Worksop, Nottinghamshire and raised in Nigeria. She was a finalist for the Million Writers award (2015), has been shortlisted for the Shirley Jackson Awards (2015), the Caine Prize for African Literature (2017 & 2020) and won the inaugural Curtis Brown First Novel prize, as well as a Nommo Award for Speculative Fiction (2020). She tweets as @chemelumadu.

NINA K. FELLOWS is a young academic, musician, and writer living in Manchester. As a psychology researcher, her work has included studies of Spiritualist mediumship, women and madness in psychiatric history, and Lacanian psychoanalytic theory. She is currently working on her first manuscript.

JANE HARTSHORN is a writer based in London. Her work explores the relationship between chronic illness and sexual identity, and she has been published in *amberflora*, *para-text*, and *Front Horse*. Her pamphlet *Tract* was published in 2017 by Litmus Publishing. She is Poetry Editor at *Ache* Magazine. @jeahartshorn

VERITY HOLLOWAY is the author of novels *Pseudotooth* and *Beauty Secrets of The Martyrs*, and *The Mighty Healer*, a biography of her Victorian quack doctor cousin. Her short stories and poems have been variously published, and her story 'Cremating Imelda' was nominated for the Pushcart Prize. She currently lives in Suffolk.

LOUISE KENWARD is a writer, artist and psychologist. Louise left the NHS in 2013 and now runs and collaborates on freelance projects, often combining arts and health. She has an MA in Fine Art (2011) from London Metropolitan University and an MSc in Criminological Psychology (1997) from Birmingham University. She is currently writing her first book *A Trail of Breadcrumbs*.

NATASHA KINDRED is often found in the company of headless saints, holy ghosts, illuminated manuscripts and various ecclesiastical oddities. She is a writer, bookseller, and recovering addict living in London with a passion for strange folklore, spontaneous adventures, slinging paint around, wildly optimistic naivety, orchids and other otherworldly pursuits.

MARION MICHELL is a London-based visual artist, blogger, writer. She has severe M.E. and for years created in the supine. As worsening health leaked function from clever hands, she now pours her art into writing. In December 2016 her book *SUPINELY SUBLIMELY* (poetic prose) was published by Palewell Press.

KATE MURDOCH (cover art) is an artist living and working in London and works predominantly in the medium of assemblage, collage and installation. Murdoch's work centres around a lifelong passion for collecting – found objects, images and other materials, mostly from the everyday and dating from the last century. www.katemurdochartist.com

IRENOSEN OKOJIE is a Nigerian British writer. Her debut novel *Butterfly Fish* won a Betty Trask award and was shortlisted for an Edinburgh International First Book Award. Her work has been featured in *The New York Times, The Observer, The Guardian*, the

BBC and the *Huffington Post*, amongst other publications. Her short stories have been published internationally including Salt's *Best British Short Stories* 2017 and 2020, *Kwani?* and *The Year's Best Weird Fiction*. She was presented at the London Short Story Festival by Booker Prize winning author Ben Okri as a dynamic talent and featured in the *Evening Standard Magazine* as one of London's exciting new authors. Her short story collection *Speak Gigantular*, published by Jacaranda Books, was shortlisted for the Edgehill Short Story Prize, the Jhalak Prize, the Saboteur Awards and nominated for a Shirley Jackson Award. She is a fellow of the Royal Society of Literature. Her new collection of stories, *Nudibranch* published by Little Brown's Dialogue Books, was longlisted for the Jhalak Prize. She is the winner of the 2020 AKO Caine Prize for Fiction for her story, 'Grace Jones'. www.irenosenokojie.com Twitter: @IrenosenOkojie

NICI WEST is an editor, short story writer and freelance copywriter. She edits works of fiction, memoir and arts journalism and her short stories have been published in places such as Dark Ink Press, Dark Lane Press and Forest Publishing. She was shortlisted for the Willesden Herald short story prize and Highly Commended for the Bridport Prize 2019. She has an MA in Creative Writing from the University of Manchester, studying under authors Geoff Ryman and Colm Toibin.

SUPPORTERS

This collection was possible with thanks to 165 backers who supporters us on Kickstarter, with special thanks to:

Leila Abu el Hawa

Clare Best

Gary Budden

Michael Carpenter

David and Claire

Maria Dorman

Laura Elliott

Sean F. Smith

Jenny Ferguson

Sarah Garnham

Dan Greensall

Heather Hubbard

Dan Jenkins

Benjamin Judge

John and Judith

William Knox-Walker

Faye Lipson Powell

Gabi May

Lucie McKnight Hardy

Ellen Mellor

Sam Mills

Emma Partridge

Cheryl Powell

Alexa Radcliffe-Hart

Larissa Reid

Jane Roberts

Fat Roland

Deaven Shade

Esther Sparrow

Nas St. Malone

Uncle Steve

Paul & Laura Trinies

Mark Urry

Luschka van Onselen

Elizabeth Varley

Baldry

ABOUT BOUDICCA PRESS

Boudicca Press is an independent publisher who celebrates the strength, courage and literary talents of women. They publish weird, literary and relationship fiction by women in the UK.

www.boudiccapress.com

ABOUT DISTURBING THE BEAST

Disturbing the Beast is a collection of weird fiction stories by some of the best women writers in the UK, featuring Kirsty Logan, Aliya Whiteley and other talented up-and-coming writers. It's the debut collection from the new literary press, Boudicca Press, who celebrate the strength, courage and literary talents of women.

The Disturbing the Beast collection explores lesser talked about female-centred topics including sexual abuse, pregnancy issues and body image. Boudicca is keen to unearth these subjects in a healthy and respectful way, something they feel is not often considered in mainstream, contemporary literature. They want to celebrate women's voices in the weird fiction genre, in a publishing industry where they feel women are under-represented.

Buy a copy at www.boudiccapress.com

ACKNOWLEDGEMENTS

Thanks to Kickstarter supporters and everyone who helped make this happen, Verity and Louise, Aliya for reading submissions, everyone who submitted their personal pieces, Georgina Bruce for help at the start and all of our supporters on social media who helped make this book happen!